The Essence of Time

The Essence of Time

by
Enzo Tiezzi

WITPRESS Southampton, Boston

Enzo Tiezzi
University of Siena, Italy

Published by

WIT Press
Ashurst Lodge, Ashurst, Southampton, SO40 7AA, UK
Tel: 44 (0) 238 029 3223; Fax: 44 (0) 238 029 2853
E-Mail: witpress@witpress.com
http://www.witpress.com

For USA, Canada and Mexico

Computational Mechanics Inc
25 Bridge Street, Billerica, MA 01821, USA
Tel: 978 667 5841; Fax: 978 667 7582
E-Mail: info@compmech.com
US site: http://www.compmech.com

British Library Cataloguing-in-Publication Data

A Catalogue record for this book is available
from the British Library

ISBN: 1-85312-949-6
ISSN: 1467-9581

Library of Congress Catalog Card Number: 2002101095

Contents

Foreword

FROM A SPACE
TO A TIME CULTURE

by Nobel Prize Winner Professor Ilya Prigogine

It is a pleasure to write a short foreword to this new book by my friend Enzo Tiezzi.

The first part of this book deals with the passage 'from a space to a time culture'. This is indeed an essential part of the scientific revolution we are witnessing at the end of the twentieth century. Science is a dialogue with nature. Over the past this dialogue has taken many forms. We feel that we are at the end of the period which started with Galileo, Copernicus and Newton and culminated in the discovery of quantum mechanics and relativity. This is a glorious period but it led, in spite of all its marvellous achievements to an oversimplified picture of nature, a picture which neglected essential aspects. Classical science emphasized stability, order and equilibrium. Today we discover everywhere instabilities and fluctuations. Our view of nature is changing dramatically.

At all levels of nature we see the emergence of 'narrative elements'. We are reminded of Scheherazade, who interrupts her beautiful story to start another one, even more beautiful. In nature we also have the cosmological history which includes the history of matter, the history of life, of humans and so on until we come to our individual history associated with our consciousness. At all levels we observe events associated with the emergence of novelties, which we may associate with the creative power of nature.

These narrative historical aspects are part of *complexity*. Complex systems share the feature of exhibiting a great variety of behaviors. Take an example from chemistry: the Belousov-Zabotinsky reaction. The details are irrelevant here, but let us suppose that there are two species of molecules: 'red' ones and 'blue' ones; moreover they transform one into the other. The behaviour of the system depends on the external constraints. Close to equilibrium the collisions are random. There may only appear short living local flashes of color. But far from equilibrium the behaviour of this system changes radically. It becomes in succession red then blue then again red. This periodicity indicates the existence of long range correlations due to the non-equilibrium conditions. I like to say *at equilibrium matter is blind, far from equilibrium it begins to 'see'*.

How to explain this variety of behavior associated to the arrow of time? The fundamental mechanism is instability, whose principal manifestations are in turn bifurcations towards a multiplicity of states including *deterministic chaos*. It confers to the underlying system a sensitivity to perturbations of intrinsic or environmental origin present in the real world, thereby raising the problem of prediction and control of the system's behavior.

The most common evidence of complexity comes from phenomena at the *macroscopic level*. Here emphasis is placed on the origin of collective behavior in multi-unit systems giving rise to new, *emergent* properties absent at the level of the units when isolated. Instability, oscillations, chaos, pattern formation and turbulence in hydrodynamics, chemistry and optics provide typical examples.

There is increasing awareness that complexity appears also at the *microscopic level* – for example in the form of complex distribution of molecular and nuclear spectra. The very origin of irreversibility is intimately related to the intrinsic instability generated by the underlying dynamics.

Classical dynamics as well as standard quantum mechanics have been built on the paradigm of simple stable systems. As the vast majority of dynamics do not satisfy these conditions, the challenge is to elaborate formulations of dynamics applicable to these more representative systems.

Progress has been achieved along these lines and some indications are given in the concluding chapters of Tiezzi's book. The very meaning of laws of nature then changes. Instead of dealing with certitudes they now deal with 'possibilities'. The description of complex systems requires a specific vocabulary: entropy, information, bifurcation and evolution become the central themes. These are also the main themes which the reader will find in these pages.

The American philosopher R. Tarnas has written: "The passion of the western world is to reunite with the ground of its being". This passion also inhabits Tiezzi's book. The classical view of science led to a dichotomy. When in 1663 R. Hooke promulgates the status of the Royal society. He describes its aims as "to improve the knowledge of natural things and all useful Arts, Manufactures, Mechanic practices, Engines and Inventions by Experiments" and he added "not meddling with Divinity, Metaphysics, Morals, Politics, Grammar, Rhetorics or Logic". We recover already C.P. Snow's famous division into *Two cultures*. The renewed view of nature which emerges today will hopefully overcome this opposition between interest in nature on one side, in man on the other. This I believe, is also the main message expressed by Professor Tiezzi.

His book is written with communicative enthusiasm and will greatly contribute to transmit to a larger public, the new changed view of nature. Time is no more opposing man to nature but on the contrary marks his belonging to an inventive and creative universe.

I. Prigogine

1

BARON VON MÜNCHHAUSEN
AND MAXWELL'S DEVIL

*"Tempus item per se non est, sed rebus ab ipsis
consequitur sensus, transactum quid sit in aevo,
tumquae res instet, quid porro deinde sequatur."*

Lucretius, *De rerum natura*, I-459-461.*

The Baron's pigtail

It is told that Baron von Münchhausen and his horse were once about to
sink into a marsh. The Baron explained his escape: "I would certainly
have died, had not the force of my arm, grasping me by my pigtail, pulled
me out of the mud together with my horse, which I held firmly between
my legs."

Paul Watzlawick[1] uses this metaphor to tackle the problems of the
logical dichotomy between 'within' and 'without' in place of the classical
'true' and 'false' and relative to the possibility of getting out, in the
broadest sense, of the world framework in order to be able to see it 'with
new eyes'. This type of approach is important for ecology of the mind,
the role of relations in systems and processes of knowledge in general. To
rely on the Baron's pigtail, however, could put us back in the mud of a
planet increasingly offended by man's technologies and cheated of the
wealth of the marvellous number of relations created by evolutionary
history, present today as biodiversity, natural capital and biological
complexity in the natural world that surrounds us. I should therefore like
to invert Watzlawick's metaphor and use it in the environmental context

---

* Time per se does not exist; the sense of what has been done in the past, what is in
the present and what will be is embodied in things themselves.

[1] P. Watzlawick, *Münchhausen zopf oder psychotherapie und 'wirklichkeit'*, Verlag Hans Huber,
Bern, 1988.

as an example of an anthropocentric attitude contrary to an awareness that we are an integral part of the co-evolutionary history of our planet. The separation between mind and nature is a bad habit of our arrogant, late twentieth-century thought.

It amuses me to counteract Baron von Münchhausen with Dersu Uzala, the little man of the tundra in the film by Akira Kurosawa, with his profound understanding of the secrets of the forest and a deep, sacred respect that harmoniously fuses courage and fear, certainty and uncertainty. Kurosawa's story adds modern ecological tension to a naturalistic account in the style of Flaherty,[2] offering the right context for an attempt at a history and interpretation of our planet.

The adventure of biological evolution is marked by chance events and exact choices; it is a *stochastic adventure* in the etymological meaning of the word, from the Greek *stokazomai,* to 'aim at the target' in archery. The arrows are distributed in an apparently random way around the bullseye, but the hand of the archer chooses, as well as he can, the direction of the arrow; the system combines chance with selection. Dersu Uzala was a good archer; let us keep him in mind as an antidote against bad mental habits.

A delicate interplay

"With a delicate interplay of weights and counterweights, nature oscillates this way and that, giving rise to a here and a there, an above and a below, a before and an after, that condition all manifestations in space and time."

This is how Goethe[3] introduces the knot of relations that bind the

---

[2] Robert Joseph Flaherty (1884-1951), American film director of Irish origin. After studying mining engineering at the Upper College of Canada and the Michigan College of Mines, from 1910 he explored the Arctic lands of North America. This was where, in documenting his travels, he gained experience in cinematography. In 1920-22, financed by a French fur company which had commissioned a film for advertising purposes, he made the film *Nanook of the North*. In 1923-26, Paramount engaged him for a film in the south seas, *Moana*. After other American experiences, including *Taboo* (1931) directed with Friedrich Murnau, he became disillusioned with Hollywood and went to England, where he animated the British documentary school. There he directed *The Man of Aran* (1934) which portrays the life of fishermen of the Aran Isles, a few miles off the western coast of Ireland.

[3] J.W. von Goethe, La teoria dei colori, compiled by Renato Troncon, with introduction by G.C. Argan, Il Saggiatore, Milan, 1979.

manifestations of nature in space and time, manifestations that have to do with the transformation of matter and energy. The four main principles with which the present essay is concerned are *energy, matter, space and time*, although time will be examined more closely. Obviously many scientific essays have been concerned with energy, matter, space and time. The ambition and in a sense originality of this essay is that it does not study the four principles themselves, but in terms of their relations and *co-evolution of relations* in the framework of the biosphere and its biological evolution. This is why the epistemological basis is completely different from, and in many cases incomparable with mechanistic, reductionist, determinist and nature-centred approaches and with anthropo-centric and observer-based approaches. The aim is not to take the point of view of the subject or object studied or of the relation that modifies both, but to study the relation itself. I will use neologisms such as ecodynamic, negentropy (E. Schrödinger),[4] emergy (H.T. Odum).[5] These words are part of the alphabet of ecology; they are as important as they are unusual in everyday literature.

A guiding concept will be that of entropy (and negentropy) and its relations with energy, probability and information. But even in this case entropy will be treated as a function which organizes and disorganizes relations between matter and energy, as well as their distribution in space and evolution in time. Time, in turn, will not be seen as an external parameter (for example entropy as a mere function of time), but as a function internal to entropy and hence internal to the co-evolutionary history of matter, energy and the biosphere. Time will be seen as the number of relations contained in the space that surrounds us.

In physics, the epistemological reference is therefore close to the latest theories of Ilya Prigogine,[6] in biology to those of Gregory Bateson[7] and Howard Odum,[5] and in philosophy to the ideas of Edgar Morin.[8] Many of the ideas in this essay are the products of chats, meetings and seminars with Morin, Odum and Prigogine as friends.

The reference point of this essay is not the universe of infinite spaces or the universe within us, but the biosphere, the earth's crust on which

---

[4] E. Schrödinger, *What is life? The physical aspects of the living cells*, Cambridge University Press, Cambridge, 1944.

[5] H.T. Odum, *Systems ecology*, J. Wiley, New York, 1983.

[6] I. Prigogine and I. Stengers, *Entre le temps et l'eternité*, Fayard, Paris, 1988.

[7] G. Bateson, *Mind and nature: a necessary unity*, Dutton, New York, 1979.

[8] E. Morin, *Per uscire dal ventesimo secolo*, Pierluigi Lubrina Editore, Bergamo, 1989.

we live, the peel of this beautiful 'blue orange'; the relations concern living creatures and matter, energy flows and biological time, their synergies and diversity.

The branch of science dealing with energy flows in biological systems is bioenergetics. It was developed in particular by Harold Morowitz at the Department of Molecular Biochemistry and Biophysics of Yale University. The physics necessary for a total understanding of bioenergetics does not exist as a finite structure, according to Morowitz.[9] The role of adenosine triphosphate (ATP) in the energy mechanisms of biological systems is known; the ubiquity of this molecule in the essential functions implying energy is known (synthesis, transport, movement, transmission and storage); but all known physical theories, from quantum mechanics to statistical mechanics, from classical thermodynamics to relativity, fail when we try to describe the evolution in time of a cell, a living system or especially an ecosystem. They fail in the attempt to provide indications for the synthesis of a living cell and they fail in the interpretation of the role of time in relation to matter and energy, treating time as an external parameter (such as ds/dt) or as a reversible parameter (evidently untrue in the biosphere that we know).

On a microscopic level, according to Morowitz, we know that there is continuous molecular movement due to thermal energy, but elegant molecular models based on X-ray diffraction or nuclear magnetic resonance give us static solutions, mediated in time. We know that molecular structure has fantastic vibrational, rotational and oscillatory movements but spectroscopic models again give solutions mediated in time and offer us a static vision. We know that a biological cell pulses, moves, lives, but the impression we receive from the most sophisticated biochemical techniques is a static one. We know that living species and ecosystems evolve and are not the same from one minute to the next, but our bad habits of thought lead us to believe the dogma of the reproducible experiment.

The paradox, very similar to that of Prigogine of the time that arises from non-time, lies in the evidence of the precise order of molecular biology, despite the continuous disorder induced by thermal motion.

The role played by relations, understood as structures that organize themselves and transmit information to other structures, is evident. Two important concepts useful for understanding the nature of biological

---

[9] H. Morowitz, *Foundation of bioenergetics*, Academic Press, New York, 1978.

relations are the 'relational order'[**] of Stebbins[10] and the 'connecting structures' of Gregory Bateson.[7] These concepts bring us to the heart of the question, a "gestalt" switch from being to becoming.

Two other fundamental steps in the direction of understanding time were the introduction of the concept of entropy, a milestone of modern physics, and the recent theories of Ilya Prigogine[11] on 'internal time' and the theorem of Poincaré. These two aspects will be examined in the chapters that follow, after a discussion of entropy, photosynthesis, ecological energetics, negentropy and global models of the biosphere, as a transition to an ecodynamic interpretation of the biosphere.

What is entropy?[12]

Let us consider a heap of stones in a field. Reading the words 'heap of stones' we all think of many stones piled on top of each other, but each of us imagines a slightly different form, as the stones may be different and piled up in different ways. If we organize the pile in a particular way, lining up the stones to form walls with the occasional space, then we call it a house with windows and doors. This is a more useful disposition than the random one; the stones have an ordered configuration according to a predetermined criterion. If we abandon the heap of stones and return after several months or years, it will presumably still be a heap of stones, though it may have changed shape. The stones may be more scattered, but it is difficult to believe that with time and the action of wind and passers-by, this heap could assume the characteristics of a house. If, on the other hand, we abandon a house, it is very likely to end up as a heap of stones. Hence there is a spontaneous passage from order to disorder.

Let us take another example. Suppose we have two containers

[**] The systematic ordering of the basic components or units of any structure is correlated with similar orders in other similar structures, enabling the structures to cooperate in specific functions, e.g. the synthesis of sugar by photosynthesis. Relational order helps organisms to carry out chemical reactions and to cause coordinated movement of the parts (thermodynamics and kinetics).

[10] G.L. Stebbins, *The basis of progressive evolution*, University of North Carolina Press, Chapel Hill, 1969.

[11] I. Prigogine, in: C. Rossi and E. Tiezzi, eds., *Ecological physical chemistry*, Elsevier, Amsterdam, 1991, pp. 1-24.

[12] For more details see E. Tiezzi and S. Ulgiati, *Entropia e dintorni*, in the school series *Alfabeti per l'ecologia*, compiled by E. Tiezzi, Giunti Marzocco, Florence, 1992.

separated by a dividing wall, with a red gas in one and a yellow gas in the other (or a hotter and a colder gas). If we remove the divider, the gases tend to mix until uniform distribution is achieved, namely an orange gas (or thermal equilibrium). If the gases were originally mixed, we would never expect them to spontaneously separate into red gas on one side and yellow on the other. The orange situation is that of greatest disorder. So this example, too, shows a spontaneous transformation towards disorder, a passage from the less to the more probable configuration.

This is a constant trend in the universe; all phenomena involving an increase in disorder are spontaneous, whereas those in which disorder decreases require an external agent and would never occur in an isolated system. We can repeat the experiment of the red and yellow gases an infinite number of times and we will always have the same result. In the same way, perfume diffuses from an open bottle into the room, but we would never see the perfume molecules go back into the bottle. A drop of ink in a glass of water and countless other situations behave in the same way.

Once the state of greatest disorder is reached, the situation seems to be irreversible, or at least it is not possible to return spontaneously to the initial conditions. Theoretically there is a probability (extremely low and never occurring as far as we know in the history of man) that the coloured gases return into their original containers. Why should the surface of a lake not freeze in the middle of summer? Although there is no reason why the lake should not give out its heat instead of absorbing heat from the sun, it never happens. The concept that heat flows spontaneously from hot to cold bodies is based on the extreme improbability that cold molecules (the water) give up their heat to hotter ones (the air).

However there is nothing to stop an external intelligence from intervening to create order; the recycling of wastes, the separation of metals by means of electromagnets, the recycling of glass with the use of centrifuges and differential waste collection, the separation of plastics by other mechanical means and the transformation of the organic fraction into biogas or fuel alcohol by fermentation processes, are complex forms of external intervention capable of reinvesting degraded materials with their original possibilities. Certain bacteria (such as those of the genus *Thiobacillus*) leach minerals, enabling greater quantities of metals to be extracted than by using mechanical methods, even when the ore contains other minerals. Copper and uranium are extracted bacteriologically in many US mines. These bacteria are an external agent capable of ordering metal dust, that is, of selecting the desired particles of metal from a mixture of rocks. When we freeze water, we act as an external agent to bring about an event that we have categorically denied could happen spontaneously, namely the passage of heat from a colder to a hotter body.

These examples are sufficient to show the parallel that exists between apparently different phenomena; the elimination of inequalities, the evening out of differences in level, the loss of identity and order in favour of non-differentiation and disorder, the tendency of energy to degrade, are different aspects of this characteristic of nature. We call this style 'entropy', and its formulation was a milestone in the application of physics to ecosystems. The universal physical law which deals with the concept of entropy is the Second Law of Thermodynamics.

Biological systems seem to violate the Second Law; they have an extremely ordered structure which evolves in the direction of greater order or less entropy. The contradiction is only an apparent one. The entropy balance must be global; it must include the organism (plant or animal) and the environment with which the organism continuously exchanges energy and matter. This is true when what we call an external agent intervenes; the tree grows because of solar energy, animals grow and reproduce because of the chemical energy contained in food, organisms develop and live by virtue of the increase in entropy that they provoke in the surrounding environment. If plants decrease in entropy as they grow, the entropy of the environment increases by a greater amount so that the change in total entropy of the plant-environment system is positive. The entropy of the universe increases and the Second Law is not violated.

It is necessary to distinguish between isolated systems (which cannot exchange energy or matter with the outside), closed systems (which exchange energy but not matter, such as our planet) and open systems (which exchange both energy and matter). A city or an organism are open systems. For a correct interpretation of the processes of open systems, it is necessary to calculate the negative entropy (or order) produced inside the system and also the positive entropy (or disorder) created by it in the external environment. In this way it becomes evident that the increase in order is only an apparent one; it occurs at the expense of the order of the surrounding environment. There is a net increase in disorder.

The apparent divergence between biological evolution's trend towards increasingly complex and ordered forms and that of the universe towards maximum entropy and disorder can be explained not only as a flow of degraded energy from the planet towards space (positive entropy) but also by the fact that the Second Law of Thermodynamics applies to systems near equilibrium. As we shall see shortly, the earth's crust, the matrix of biological evolution, is a physical system of quite another type.

Schrödinger's negentropy

Many regard 1944 as the year in which biophysics was founded, with the publication of Erwin Schrödinger's *What is life?*.[4] Winner of the Nobel Prize for Physics and father of quantum mechanics, in this publication Schrödinger expresses his thoughts on biological problems. He introduces the concept of negentropy, emphasizing that it is a negative variant of entropy from an initial value (the birth of the individual, the origin of life, the beginning of biological evolution) and not of absolute negative entropy, since the Third Law of Thermodynamics does not conceive of an entropy value less than zero. "How would we express in terms of the statistical theory the marvelous faculty of a living organism, by which it delays the decay into thermodynamical equilibrium (death)? We said before that it feeds on negative entropy, attracting, as it were, a stream of negative entropy upon itself, to compensate the entropy increase it produces by living and thus to maintain itself on a stationary and fairly low entropy level."

Morowitz underlines the fact that when Schrödinger says that an organism feeds on negentropy, he simply means that its existence depends on an increase in entropy in the rest of the universe. This holds for open thermodynamic systems (living organisms) and for closed systems (the planet Earth). Obviously it is not true for isolated systems, fated to 'thermal death' by entropy increase. Schrödinger's statement contains the key to the origin of life on Earth, the history of biological evolution, with its protagonist photosynthesis, the green talisman of the next chapter. It is the history of a special planet which learned to capture solar energy and feed on negentropy from the universe in order to create the ordered and dissipative structures that are living organisms.

In 1871, J.C. Maxwell proposed a paradox which embarrassed physicists for a long time. He imagined a system with a gas contained in two receptacles, A and B, at the same temperature, separated by a wall. In the wall there was a small hole guarded by a devil who separated fast molecules (hot molecules, since temperature is a measure of the movement of a molecule) from slow (cold) molecules, placing the first in A and the second in B. At the end there was a temperature difference, in apparent disagreement with the Second Law of Thermodynamics.

Today Maxwell's devil has been exorcized. We know that to do his work he would need to consume energy obtained outside the system. This is just what our planet has learned to do.

2

THE GREEN TALISMAN

The voice that spoke was certainly that of our master; he knows how to connect traces of things here and there. (...) He observed the stars and traced their positions and orbits in the sand; he kept a watch on the sea of air and never tired of considering its clarity, movements, clouds and lights. (...) He enjoyed connecting distant things. Now the stars would be men to him, now men stars, stones animals and clouds plants.

Novalis, *The Disciples of Sais*

The history of a singular planet

"A blade of grass is energy manifesting as matter, the material grass. The spirit of grass is that invisible force that produces the species grass, and that manifests to us in the form of real grass."

This Iroquois cosmogony tells us of the relation between energy and grass. More than a hundred years ago, in 1886, Ludwig Boltzmann,[1] one of the fathers of modern physical chemistry, was concerned with this relation in scientific terms. According to Boltzmann, the struggle for life is not a struggle for basic elements or energy but for the entropy (negative) available in the transfer from the hot sun to the cold Earth. Utilizing this transfer to a maximum, plants force solar energy to perform chemical reactions before it reaches the thermal level of the Earth's surface. The paths of these reactions are unexplored and still impossible to reproduce in our laboratories.

To live and reproduce, plants and animals need a continuous flow of energy. The energy of the biosphere, which originates in the luminous

---

[1] Quoted in R. Huber, A structural basis of light energy and electron transfer in biology, Nobel Lecture, *Angewandte chemie int. ed. engl.*, **28** (1989), p. 848-869.

energy of the sun, is captured by plants and passes from one living form to another along the food chain. The luminous energy captured by chlorophyll, the green pigment in plants, is stored in carbohydrates, molecules rich in energy, by a process called photosynthesis, a term meaning 'to make things with light'. This radiant pathway that provides us with great quantities of food, fibres and energy, all of solar origin, has existed for about four billion years, a long time if we think that hominids appeared on the earth only three million years ago and that known history covers only ten thousand years. The ancestors of today's plants were the blue algae, cyanobacteria, that began to practise photosynthesis, assuming a fundamental role in biological evolution.

All vegetation, whether natural or cultivated, has been capturing solar energy for millennia, transforming it into food, fibres, materials and work, and providing the basis for the life of the biosphere.

Agriculture has always been a human activity which accumulates energy in the Earth system. In this way man has not 'created' energy (in fact the First Law of Thermodynamics states that energy cannot be created or destroyed), but has only enriched the Earth with solar energy that would otherwise have been lost. The purpose of agriculture is to produce food (meat, milk, vegetables, cereals…) and materials (wool, linen, cotton, hemp, timber…), but if we look at the energy content of these products we can say that agriculture is the capturing of energy from the sun to synthesize materials and food with a high calorie content.

By far the major part of the energy received by the Earth's surface from the sun is dispersed; it is reflected, stored in the soil and water, used in the evaporation of water and so forth. Only about one per cent of the solar energy that falls on fertile land is fixed by photosynthesis in plants (grass, trees, phytoplankton) in the form of high-energy organic molecules. By biochemical processes (respiration) the plant transforms this energy into other organic compounds and work.

The food chain considered in terms of energy flows has a logic of its own; the energy degrades progressively in the different phases of the chain (plant producers, animal consumers, microbe decomposers), giving back the elementary substances necessary to build again the molecules of living cells with the help of solar energy.

The organization of living beings in mature ecosystems slows the dispersal of energy fixed by plants to a minimum, using it completely for its complex mechanisms of regulation. This is made possible by large 'reservoirs' of energy (biomasses) and by the diversification of living species. The stability of natural ecosystems, however, means that the final energy yield is zero, except for a relatively small quantity of biomass which is buried underground to form fossils for the future.

Photosynthesis counteracts entropic degradation in so far as it orders disordered matter; the plant takes up disordered material (low-energy molecules of water and carbon dioxide in disorderly agitation) and puts it in order using solar energy. It organizes the material by building it into complex structures. Photosynthesis was therefore the process which, by capturing solar energy and decreasing the entropy of the planet, paved the way for evolution. Photosynthesis is the green talisman of life, Maxwell's devil that decreases the entropy of the biosphere.

On the Earth, living systems need a continuous flow of negative entropy (that is, energy from outside) and this flow consists of that very solar energy captured by photosynthesis. This input of solar energy is what fuels the carbon cycle.

The history of life on Earth can be viewed as the history of photosynthesis and the history of evolution, as the history of a singular planet which learned to capture solar energy and feed on the negative entropy of the universe for the creation of complex structures (living organisms). Unfortunately, by wasting energy and by using technologies that run contrary to nature, man risks upsetting this vital mechanism. The limits of the photosynthetic process are not dictated by the energy source, the sun, which is practically infinite, but by the crazy methods of production currently used by man.

The sun is an enormous machine which produces energy and offers the Earth the possibility of receiving large quantities of negative entropy (organization, life), allowing a global balance which does not contradict the Second Law of Thermodynamics. Every year the sun sends the Earth 5.6×10^{24} joules of energy, more than 10,000 times more energy than mankind consumes in a year. It is as if the sun sends us 260 tons when we consume only 15 kilogrammes.

Once upon a time

Once upon a time, two million years ago, there was a hominid. Once upon a time, 120 million years ago, there was a flower in Australia; it is the oldest known fossil flower. Once upon a time, about 200 million years ago, there were dinosaurs. Once upon a time, two thousand million years ago, there were green algae. Once upon a time, 3,300 million years ago, there were the first living cells. A history of living beings and minerals, of photosynthesis and increasingly complex molecules, a history of atmospheres and water, of carbon dioxide and water vapour, of hot volcanic pools and oxygen, that did not exist before.

It is a history to measure in biological time, a history of relations and co-evolution, a history of which man is part and from which his molecular structure and his genes are derived. Jean-Paul Sartre said that man should always keep his biological origins in mind.

This history took place on a tiny planet, the Earth, with a limited surface, a limited carrying capacity, within constraints which determined and favoured biological evolution, constraints of space, temperature, atmospheric composition and speed of production that fix thresholds beyond which life cannot exist.

The constraints and carrying capacity determine dynamic equilibria and relations and are determined in turn by them. Two mechanisms are fundamental for this long and marvellous ecodynamic interplay; feedback and homeostasis. The interplay resembles the Chinese game of the scissors, stone and paper; each can defeat one of the others but there is no priority of command nor one way of playing which is superior to others.

Technological man, however, has cheated at play, deceiving biological evolution. He has given himself artificial mutations, pulling himself out of nature like Baron von Münchhausen, and becoming dominator. Technological man does not obey the equations of Lotka and Volterra which regulate equilibrium between prey and predator. With mechanical prostheses he plays like a bird, flying with aeroplanes; he can have the claws of a tiger by using firearms; he can hibernate in winter in heated houses. The point is obviously not to renounce these conquests of progress and science but to know that we have evaded the controls of feedback and homeostasis of natural biological evolution and that only we men can choose the road of survival of our species and the planet, by respecting the weaker species, the great biological cycles, biodiversity and the constraints of nature.

The life of each individual and species is part of a large-scale process involving the metabolism of the planet as a whole.[2,3] Biological activity is

---

[2] E. Tiezzi, *Tempi storici, tempi bioligici*, Garzanti, Milan, 1984.
[3] E. Tiezzi, *Il capitombolo di Ulisse*, Feltrinelli, Milan, 1991.

a planetary property, a continuous interaction of atmospheres, oceans, plants, animals, microorganisms, molecules, electrons, energies and matter, all part of a global whole. The role of each of these components is essential for the maintenance of life.

The relations and activities of the global biogeochemical system are life. The aim of modern science is to maintain these relations and characteristics, to live in harmony with nature, not to conquer it. This type of science comprehends complexity and uncertainty, it moves away from a deterministic-mechanistic view of the world in favour of a holistic and evolutionary view. As we shall see, it refers to the 'clinamen' of Lucretius and to the 'disciples of Sais' of Novalis rather than to the clockwork world of Descartes and the reversible time of Newtonian mechanics. It considers the constraints not as halters or chains but as conditions creating diversity and mutation, all of which amounts to biological evolution: constraints as sources of creativity and presuppositions for evolution.

A dangerous Venusian atmosphere

The adventure of travel is usually part of the cultural heritage of a biologist. Darwin made his discoveries sailing around the world in the *Beagle,* and Wallace had his intuitions about evolution during a psychedelic dream in the jungles of Indonesia. If you talk to a modern malacologist you will see his imagination begin to work at the mention of a study trip to the Galapagos or Philippines, or collecting liguus in the mangrove swamps of the Everglades in Florida or a visit to a shell museum founded by a Dutch lady centuries ago at Makasar, the capital of Celebes. His space is the planet.

Modern ecologists venture to Graham Land in Antarctica to collect mosses and lichens for monitoring or to study the levels of contaminants in penguins and seals. It is clear to them that the problem of pollution involves the whole planet and that the planet is the correct unit to use for the space we are concerned with. They know that our survival depends on the survival of the planet as a whole. The holistic approach is a scientific necessity for ecology and especially for photosynthesis, a mechanism that concerns the whole biosphere.

Two molecules play an essential role in photosynthesis: ozone and carbon dioxide. A decrease in the former in the ozone layer could lead to the inhibition of photosynthesis by ultraviolet rays; an increase in the latter in the atmosphere could lead to inhibition of the exchange of degraded energy (heat, positive entropy) with the rest of the universe due to the increased greenhouse effect.

The atmosphere of Venus is 96.5% carbon dioxide, a quantity lethal for any form of life because it determines a surface temperature of more than 400°C. By contrast, the Earth's atmosphere is 0.033% carbon dioxide, just enough to ensure warm springs and hot summers. However, the concentration of carbon dioxide in the Earth's atmosphere has increased from about 290 ppm (parts per million) to about 350 ppm in the last fifty years. This is an enormous increase in such an infinitesimally brief moment in the scale of biological time. The main cause of the increase is the use of fossil fuels. These release about 5.4 gigatons (1015 grammes) of carbon into the atmosphere in a year. The second cause is the clearing of forests at a rate of 20 million hectares per year. This releases 1.6 gigatons of carbon per year. The third cause is related to cement production with a further 0.1 gigatons per year. The natural rate of absorption of the oceans and of photosynthesis cannot keep up with the pace of technology, and the millennial equilibrium of energy flows of the biosphere is at risk for the first time in the history of the planet.

The Earth's atmosphere enabled life to form and evolution to take place; it made it possible for photosynthesis to increase the percentage of oxygen in the atmosphere two billion years ago; it originates from a long and complex history of evolutionary processes and feedbacks. Due to the 'sorcerer's apprentices' of the last fifty years, it may become a lifeless Venusian atmosphere. Complex mathematical models of the increased greenhouse effect are unable to predict how the oceans will respond, how the modified feedback mechanisms will act, how the climate will change. It is a stupid adventure for sorcerer's apprentices of an unlikely Venusian story. Evading the control of the equations of Lotka and Volterra, they are tampering with one of the vital ganglions of our biosphere. Let us bring them down to Earth!

3

THE SCIENTIFIC FOUNDATIONS
FOR A COSMOGONY

Entropy and biology

The relations between entropy (and negentropy), evolution and Boltzmann's H theorem (discussed in detail in Chapter 6) are complex and intriguing. Although we have already introduced Schrödinger's concept of negentropy and there will be some repetition in what follows, it is important to give a complete picture of the scientific basis of energy flows in the biosphere and bioenergetics in general.

Harold Morowitz[1] states the problem in the following way. Evolution implies a hierarchical trend towards increasingly complex living systems. The Second Law of Thermodynamics states that the universe, or each isolated section of it, tends towards maximum entropy. Statistical mechanics and kinetic theory tell us that maximum entropy implies maximum disorder within the framework of the constraints of the system. Hence when we think about evolution in this context (Boltzmann's H theorem),[2] we think of evolution towards increasingly disordered states of the system.

This idea is strikingly at variance with our knowledge of biology. Clearly the trend of living organisms is towards the creation of order where previously there was disorder; the trend is to organize and self-organize. Life seems to contradict the Second Law of Thermodynamics. The solution to this apparent contradiction between biological and physical theory, according to Morowitz, lies in the realization that the Second Law of Thermodynamics applies to systems that are close to

[1] H. Morowitz, *Energy flow in biology*, Ox Bow Press, Woodbridge, Connecticut, 1979.

[2] L. Boltzmann, *Lectures on gas theory*, University of California Press, Berkeley and Los Angeles, 1964, Part I, Chap. 1, paras. 5, 6.

equilibrium, whereas the surface of the Earth, the matrix of biological evolution, belongs to a different class of physical systems. Systems in equilibrium must be either adiabatic (isolated) or isothermal. The biosphere, however, is quite another type of physical system, in contact with various sources and sinks, and with matter and energy flowing through it from the sources to the sinks.

Let us consider the following flow diagram:

energy sources → intermediate system (biosphere) → sinks

Let us now consider the system divided into two parts:
1) source(s) + sink(s)
2) intermediate system(i)
According to the Second Law of Thermodynamics:

$$dS_s + dS_i \geq 0$$

where S is entropy, S_s is the entropy of source + sink and S_i is the entropy of the intermediate system. The flow of energy from the source to the sink will always involve an increase in entropy:

$$dS_s > 0$$

whereas the only restriction placed by the Second Law of Thermodynamics on dS_i is that:

$$-dS_i \leq dS_s$$

so that the entropy of the intermediate system (in our case the biosphere) can decrease if there is an energy flow. A flow of energy provides the intermediate system (the Earth's surface) with quantities of energy for the creation of states far from equilibrium, that is, far from thermal death. The farther the non-equilibrium system is from equilibrium, the more ordered it is. The ordered state of a biological system would decay, if left to itself, towards the most disorderly state possible. This is why work must continuously be done to order the system. As we have seen, this requires a hot source and a cold sink, the sun and outer space.

The surface of the Earth (intermediate system) receives a flow of energy from the sun source at 5,800°K (temperature of the surface of the sun; the core of the sun is millions of degrees hotter) and returns it to the sink of outer space at 3°K. In this vast temperature range lies the secret of life and the possibility of work against entropic equilibrium, moving the living system away from equilibrium, towards ordered, negentropic, alive states. The living system is maintained in a 'steady state' as far as possible from equilibrium by the flow of energy E.[3]

The decrease in entropy (negentropy) in the biosphere depends on its capacity to capture energy from the sun and to retransmit it into space in the form of infrared radiation (positive entropy). If retransmission were to be prevented, in other words, if the planet were shrouded in an adiabatic membrane (extreme greenhouse effect), all living processes would cease very quickly and the system would decay towards the equilibrium state, that is, towards thermal death. A sink is just as necessary for life as a source.

Morowitz continues that all biological processes depend on the absorption of solar photons and the transfer of heat to the celestial sinks. The sun would not be a negentropy source if there were not a sink for the flow of thermal energy. The surface of the Earth is at a constant total energy, re-emitting as much energy as it absorbs. The subtle point is that it is not energy per se that makes life continue but the flow of energy through the system. The global ecological system or biosphere can be defined as the part of the Earth's surface which is ordered by the flow of energy by means of the process of photosynthesis.

The physical chemistry mechanism was elegantly described by Nobel Prize winner Albert Szent-György[4] as the common knowledge that the ultimate source of all our energy and negative entropy is the sun. When a photon interacts with a particle of matter on our globe, it raises an electron or a pair of electrons to a higher energy level. This excited state usually has a brief life and the electron falls back to its basic level in

---

[3] Solar energy is distributed over its spectrum as follows (molecular changes induced in brackets): 0.02% far ultraviolet (ionization), 7.27% ultraviolet (electron transitions and ionization), 51.73% visible (electron transitions), 38.90% near-infrared (electron and vibrational transitions), 2.1% infrared (rotational and vibrational transitions). A small fraction is fixed chemically by photosynthesizing organisms. This energy is the prime mover of biological transformations, including the main nutritional cycles. Global ecological processes are characterized by chemical cycles, such as the carbon and nitrogen cycles. The solar energy reaching the Earth is about 5.6×10^{24} joules but the figure, E, normally accepted, after correction for albedo, is 3.93×10^{24} joules.

[4] A. Szent-György, in W.D. McElroy and B. Glass, editors, *Light and Life*, Johns Hopkins Press, Baltimore, 1961.

10^{-7}-10^{-8} seconds, giving up its energy in one way or another. Life has learned to capture the electron in the excited state, to uncouple it from its partner and to let it decay to its fundamental level through the biological machinery, using the extra energy for vital processes.

All biological processes, therefore, take place because they are fuelled by solar energy. Morowitz[5] notes that it is this tension between photosynthetic construction and thermal degradation that sustains the global operation of the biosphere and the great ecological cycles.

Negentropy and the gypsy

The Second Law of Thermodynamics says that the universe, or any other isolated system in the universe, tends towards maximum entropy, towards thermodynamic equilibrium understood as an absence of differences, or thermal death, in the terminology of Clausius.[6] We have also seen that statistical mechanics and kinetic theory show that maximum entropy means maximum disorder within the framework of the constraints of the system.

Boltzmann defined entropy, S, as follows:

$$S = k \ln W$$

where W is the total number of microstates possible, within the framework of macroscopic constraints.

Let us now consider the entropy of a system that is not in equilibrium. The change in entropy when a system moves towards a state of non-equilibrium is:

$$\Delta S = S_a - S = k \ln W_a / W$$

where W_a is a subset of possible states W; hence W_a / W is always less than one and the term ΔS is always negative. Hence the entropy of the state of equilibrium is maximum and the other states must have a lower entropy.

---

[5] H.J. Morowitz, *Foundations of bioenergetics*, Academic Press, New York, 1978.

[6] Rudolf Clausius must have tormented himself over the final destiny (death) "of the whole of Creation"; for a reconstruction of the intellectual journey of the Prussian scientist from the first formulation of the Second Principle to this 'cosmological' version, see M. Guillen, *Five equations that changed the world*, Little, Brown & Co., London, 1995, Chap. 5.

The non-equilibrium entropy function is expressed as:

$$S = S_{eq} + \Delta S.$$

As the system tends to equilibrium, ΔS tends to zero.

To sum up:

a) Entropy is a maximum at equilibrium and there is therefore a natural trend towards maximum entropy or maximum disorder.[7]

b) On the other hand, biological evolution implies a hierarchical trend towards increasingly complex and ordered forms of living systems.

Now we know that this is an apparent distinction only. The entropy balance must be global and must include both the biological organism and the environment with which it continuously exchanges energy and matter. Hence biological organisms develop and live by virtue of the increase in entropy that their metabolism causes in their surroundings. The global change in entropy (system + environment) is positive, the entropy of the universe increases, the Second Law is not violated.[8]

When bacteria are cultured in a glucose solution, one notices that part of the sugar causes entropy to decrease by being transformed into cell constituents, and part is transformed into carbon dioxide and water, contributing to an overall increase in entropy.

For open systems, it is necessary to combine the negative entropy produced inside the system with the positive entropy discharged into the environment, and to calculate the total change in entropy. In this way we see that although disorder sometimes seems to degenerate into order, this is only a facet of the problem, the apparent order occurring at the cost of even greater disorder in the surroundings. Living systems therefore need a continuous flow of negative entropy from outside and a sink for an even greater amount of positive entropy. Ilya Prigogine calls these open systems 'dissipative structures'. The flow of energy causes changes in dissipative structures, which reorganize towards a higher level of complexity.

The biosphere is a special kind of system. It is a closed system which exchanges energy but not matter and is in contact with a permanent and practically infinite heat source (the sun) and with a cold sink (outer space), also permanent and practically infinite, to which it gives up its

---

[7] All this follows from Boltzmann's famous H Theorem, in the context of which evolution means tending towards increasingly disordered states of the system.

[8] As we see in Chapter 11, sect. Far from equilibrium.

degraded heat. The biosphere is a steady state system because the source and sink are fixed and the flows from the source to the sink are constant in time so that the parameters of the system (temperature, pressure, and so forth) are practically independent of time. This makes life possible and is the reason why large changes induced artificially by man in periods that are brief in the scale of biological time are so dangerous.

The difference between a system in equilibrium and one in a steady state is that the latter exchanges energy and/or matter with external sinks. The stationary state and non-equilibrium states are not characterized by maximum entropy. This is why the studies of Herman Daly[9] on the economics of the steady state are fertile ground for theories on sustainable development and ecological economics. As always, we are dealing with constraints and relations that define models and systems, and as always, time is the watershed between the various points of view.

One last point: the steady state is one in which the flow of energy maintains the system as far as possible from equilibrium. The biosphere, a steady state system far from equilibrium, is in a necessary rather than an accidental state.

In the last chapter of *Chance and necessity* (1970),[10] Jacques Monod, winner of the Nobel Prize for Medicine (1965), states that the only global message of scientific enterprise is that man increasingly discovers the nonsense of his presence in the universe. If man accepts this message in all its significance, he must awaken from his millennial sleep to discover his complete solitude and absolute extraneousness. He now knows that, like the gypsy, he is at the fringe of the universe in which he lives. The universe is deaf to his music, and indifferent to his hopes, suffering and crimes. But Monod was wrong; the gypsy is not an accident but a stochastic necessity.

[9] H. Daly, *Steady state economics: the economics of biophysical equilibrium and moral growth*, W.H. Freeman & Co., San Francisco, 1977.

[10] J. Monod, *Il caso e la necessità*, Italian translation, Mondadori, Milan, 1970.

4

THE WAY OF THE HIPPOGRYPH: A FASCINATING ALTERNATIVE FOR THE ORIGINS OF LIFE

C'è qualcosa di nuovo oggi nel sole,
anzi d'antico: io vivo altrove, e sento
che sono intorno nate le viole.

(Giovanni Pascoli, *L'aquilone*)

Hopeful monster

I use 'hippogryph' as a metaphor for diversity, 'hopeful monster', or creative mutation as a metaphor for non-obligatory, non-repetitive direction, a path on which one does not meet cloned and replicating individuals, biotechnological dogmas and mechanistic paradigms aimed at erasing nature's diversity and at showing nature as a molecular machine, as boring as a clock and perfectly undifferentiated.[1]

---

[1] As far back as 1933, R. Goldschmidt, in 'Some aspects of evolution' (*Science*, **78**, 539-547) warned that we should not forget that what looks like a monster today may be the start of a new line of adaptation of the species (...). He emphasized the importance of the rare but important mutations involving decisive embryonic processes that can give rise to what we may call monsters but which could be successful, monsters that would begin a new evolutionary line if they could adapt to some empty environmental niche. Karl Popper, in *Conoscenza oggettiva* (Italian translation, Armando, Rome, 1978), notes that Goldschmidt does not break with the idea of natural selection but with the idea that any evolutionary mutation must be explainable in terms of a large number of small variations. Goldschmidt assumes that large mutations occasionally occur. These are usually lethal and are eliminated, but some may survive. This explains genuine differences and the obvious affinity between the various forms of life. He describes the large mutations as monsters that may succeed. Following a suggestion from Popper, Imre Lakatos used the concept of hopeful monster for ideas which challenge the intellectual status quo, but nevertheless

A possible way of the hippogryph, within the limits of this metaphor of mine, was described by the English biophysicist Freeman Dyson, now at Princeton, in his *Origins of life*.[2] Starting from the lessons of Schrödinger in Dublin in 1943 and the theories of Eigen, and using the mathematics of von Neumann and the biology of Margulis, Dyson constructed a model envisaging the transition from chaos to a state of organized metabolic activity in a molecular population sufficiently rich to ensure homeostasis.

On this pathway let us imagine two hippogryphs strolling or flying, two completely different protagonists of biological evolution. The first is called 'proteins' and the second 'nucleic acids'. Let us begin to read their history. The two hippogryphs are of different ages; one is older, but not the one we should expect.

Referring to Schrödinger's *What is life?*,[3] Dyson makes the distinction between the mechanism of replication and that of metabolism. Both these phenomena, according to Dyson, have a conceptual basis in physics: replication by virtue of the quantum mechanical stability of molecular structures, metabolism by virtue of the capacity of a living cell to obtain negative entropy from its surroundings, in accordance with the laws of thermodynamics.

Dyson then aims a shot at Schrödinger, stating that *What is life?* favours the replication approach, one of the bases for this being the then recent discovery by Delbrück of purely parasitic bacteriophages that had lost all metabolic functions and retained only the function of replication. According to Dyson, Schrödinger sees the world of biology with the eyes of Delbrück (with due respect to the latter's profound intuitions and basic research) and has a concept of the living organism as being very similar to a bacteriophage. Dyson concludes that this line of reasoning, starting from the facts of biological replication and ending in the quantum mechanical structure of the gene, was brilliant, and was taken as a model in all subsequent molecular biology research.

I do not agree with this criticism of Schrödinger, one reason perhaps

---

find an intellectual niche in which to grow (see part I of his *Dimostrazioni e confutazioni. La logica della scoperta matematica*, J. Worrall, E. Zahar eds., Italian translation, Feltrinelli, Milan, 1979). Lakatos used Goldschmidt's heuristic suggestion to characterize the growth of mathematical knowledge; I think it could be useful in the more general context of an ecology of ideas or culture.

    [2] F. Dyson, *Origins of life*, Cambridge University Press, Cambridge, 1985.
    [3] E. Schrödinger, *What is life? The physical aspects of the living cells*, Cambridge University Press, Cambridge, 1944.

being that as a physical chemist, I discern the ingenious intuition of negentropy in *What is life?*, and the thermodynamic basis for interpreting biological evolution. On the other hand, it is true that genetic engineering and molecular biology see only with the eyes of Delbrück and that until a few years ago molecular genetics considered the life of an organism to be nothing but the faithful translation of the programme written in DNA. Such a view likens nature to a predictable and eventually controllable machine.

Today we know that this is not true, that the predictability of life is an illusion, that DNA changes even during the life of an organism, that it can be read in different ways and that the changes depend on the overall functioning of, and on a dense network of interactions between, the components of living beings, and between them and the environment. Today we know that life is a set of relations and co-evolutions reaching us from distant biological eras, an infinite set of interactions between molecules and cells, between atmospheres and living beings, between biological species and ecosystems, and we know that life is more characteristic of these systemic interactions than of a single individual. Lucretius was right; life is passed from one thing to another, given in property to no one but for the use of all.

Today we know that just as we cannot imagine metabolic life without replication, we cannot imagine replicative life without metabolism. Dyson was right; defending biodiversity means opposing the destruction of the relations and histories that created differences. Replication alone means the risk of having many things which are all the same and with the same history. Metabolism, stochastic encounters with the environment and negentropy, however, play a historical-creative role in biological evolution. The new creativity is stabilized and transmitted by DNA.

Gianluca Bocchi and Mauro Ceruti recount in their usual fascinating way the origins of stories,[4] defining coevolution as a history of interactions between systems (and between what we define from time to time as systems and environment), and a history of reciprocal compatibilities that develop between them or fail. Dyson identifies two origins of histories of life: that of proteins, the hardware of the computer that physically processes information, and that of nucleic acids, the sophisticated software that contains and transmits information. Life began twice, with different creatures, one capable of metabolism, the other of

---

[4] G. Bocchi and M. Ceruti, *Origini di storie*, Feltrinelli, Milan, 1993.

replication. Then they met, perhaps much later, a long time ago: a meeting favoured by chance, but less improbable than simultaneous origin.

In other words, if the spontaneous appearance of a protein structure is an improbable event in the midst of molecular chaos, if the spontaneous appearance of a nucleic acid structure is also unlikely, the two improbable events, Dyson emphasizes, are more likely to occur independently over a long span of time than together. Hence the first organisms were probably cells with a metabolic apparatus controlled by proteins and devoid of genetic apparatus; the first organisms consisting exclusively of proteins could have lived independently for a long time, gradually developing a more and more efficient metabolic apparatus.

Histories, encounters and relations are favoured by time, real time, an intrinsic property of matter. Time moulds forms, leaving traces of encounters, the footprints of past relations. Nature, rich with information and evolutionary history, allows new encounters and new diversities; it allows hippogryphs to meet at Prigogine's crossroads.

It is not a question of choosing between different hypotheses; science is the cemetery of hypotheses. Aleksandr Oparin, Cairns-Smith and Manfred Eigen adduce data and arguments that are more than convincing in favour of their three different theories on the origin of life.

Oparin, the Russian who in 1924, at the age of 30 years, wrote *Preishozdemie zizni* (*The origin of life*)[5] was elected president of the International Society for the Study of the Origins of Life in the splendid French abbey at Pont à Mousson. In July 1993, Eigen delivered a fascinating opening lecture at the International Congress on Biophysics in Budapest. Cairns-Smith[6] started with clay and the role of metals and ended up in a position similar to Dyson on the double origins of life.

Paradoxically, Oparin does not use thermodynamics, although entropic considerations would have helped his argument. Entropic constraints and limited resources favour creativity and evolution in the direction of complexity. According to Dyson, the creativity that unfolds almost by chance in complicated structures is more important as a moving force of evolution than Darwinian competition between replicating monads.

This may be the motive underlying the epigraph at the beginning of Oparin's book:

---

[5] A.I. Oparin, *Preishozdenie zizni,* Izdatel'stvo Moskovskij rabocij , Moscow, 1924.

[6] A.G. Cairns-Smith, *Seven clues to the origin of life,* Cambridge University Press, Cambridge, 1985.

"Every theory, dear friend, is grey,
and green the golden tree of life." (Goethe)

Ring, beautiful ring of mine

The multiplicity of life was chosen by nature a long time ago. At Burgess, in western Canada, more than a hundred species belonging to eighteen different zoological types, from 500 million years ago, were found in the same archaeological deposit. In the field of palaeontology, discoveries showing the vastness of the mystery of evolutionary history and opening new horizons for our hypotheses emerge from the dawn of biological time. Archaeology continually confronts us with new mysteries. In Alaska, Palaeoindians different from the populations that arrived in the Americas from Siberia have been discovered. They were prehistoric mammoth hunters from about 12,000 years ago. They had objects, arms and a culture completely different from the other populations of the area; so many histories, so many origins of history, all interwoven with the environment but with different networks of relations and different times.

The discovery that the oldest known microfossils, preserved in stromatolites, are a complex ecosystem of photosynthetic organisms, suggested to Morowitz, Deamer and Smith an interpretation of biogenesis as an evolutionary process; the resulting model was recently published in the *Journal of molecular evolution.*[7] Starting from the assumption that biogenesis went from simplicity to complexity and that the ancestor of the stromatolite organisms, probably the universal ancestor, must have developed from disorganized (high entropy) matter over a period of several hundred million years, the authors postulate an evolutionary process based on the self-replication of vesicles (by rupture of vesicles that had grown too big, or fusion by collision of undersize vesicles) on the basis of chemical processes and energy transmission mechanisms (given the availability of a source of free energy). In other words, primordial radiation may have led to the universal ancestor and the system of vesicles described above has the properties required for selecting favourable molecular events, even though the information was not yet stored in a macromolecular genetic apparatus. The peculiar characteristic of this model is that it allows macromolecules to be a consequence of

---

[7] H.J. Morowitz, D.W. Deamer and T. Smith, Biogenesis as an evolutionary process, *Journal of molecular evolution*, **33**, 207, Springer Verlag, New York, 1991.

evolutionary processes rather than a prerequisite for them.

To focus attention again on metabolic processes simply means underlining the fact that all living organisms feed on energy and chemical substances; it means stressing again the primary role of negentropy; it also means reasoning in terms of open and dissipative systems, along the lines of Prigogine's thermodynamics, as we shall see in detail in the following chapters. Metabolism, time, negentropy and interactions with the environment create diversity. Diversity is life; what sense would life have without diversity?

As children we played a game that we called 'Ring, beautiful ring of mine'. The game consisted in passing a ring hidden between the palms of the hands around a circle of friends and guessing who had it in the end. My friends were Bettino, Fabio, Flavio, Lido and Nedo: five different people. If we had been five cloned Lidos, there would have been no point to the game. I think that there can be much confusion between logical types. If attention were focused on the ring, a determinist scientist would be content to know where the ring was, its quantum state, irrespective of whether the states were five Lidos all the same or Bettino, Fabio, Flavio, Lido and Nedo. However, really guessing where the ring was meant not only trying to find out in whose hands it was, but also knowing the five people that played the game, and being able to call them by different names. A game between cloned individuals would have been a great bore.

Would not an Earth with flowers all the same or fruit all of the same size, forged by genetic engineering with the sole aim of profit, be grey and lifeless? Genetic history is beautiful because it was played stochastically and not manipulated. To centre the bets of the science of the future only on replication could be a dangerous game. Who is to say that life is based only on DNA? The Earth is alive, the biosphere is a living system and the Earth, we know, does not have DNA and cannot replicate. For this reason, too, it should be kept as it is, unless we believe in the ironic model presented at the Conference on Ecological Economics in Stockholm by a Canadian scientist. The initial postulate of the model was: "Let us suppose that we have two planets...".

5

SPIN

Minimum effects

Why does the Earth rotate anticlockwise rather than clockwise? Luke Dones and Scott Tremaine answer this question in the journal *Science*,[1] ascribing the Earth's anomalous rotation to a chance collision with a body about the size of Mars, which was also responsible for the formation of the Moon. The Moon in its turn stabilized the present inclination of the Earth, according to Lasker, Joutel and Robutel in *Nature*.[2] The Moon has therefore played an essential part in maintaining our present climate with its changing seasons and in permitting life to emerge. Encounters and relations are always important; the tides and wine-making are not the only things that depend on the close relation between the Earth and the Moon.

The questions we should be considering today concern small things, often wrongly ignored, and relations that occurred aeons ago, which are part of our distant biological history. The memory of these small things shapes present relations. The flutter of a butterfly wing[3] that provokes a cyclone in a different place at a different time is emblematic of the small things; the rotation and inclination of the Earth which determine our seasons and climate are examples of historic relations. When we consider these two aspects together, we realize the single-minded stupidity of playing down the importance of the changes that man is inducing in the biosphere, changes that range from the increased greenhouse effect to erosion, from the hole in the ozone layer to acid rain.

---

[1] L. Dones and S. Tremaine, "Why does the Earth spin forward?", *Science*, **259**, 1993, 350-354.

[2] J. Laskar, F. Joutel, P. Robutel, "Stabilization of the Earth's obliquity by the Moon", *Nature*, **361**, 1993, 615-617.

[3] The so-called butterfly effect, well known in the deterministic chaos literature, exemplifies far-from-equilibrium dynamics, or systems which are highly sensitive to initial conditions. See also Chapter 11.

On the one hand we have the magnitude of the age of the universe: from 13 to 18 billion years; on the other the minuteness of the building units of matter: a human hair is a million times thicker than an atom, the latter ten thousand times larger than its nucleus; nuclei are ten times bigger than protons and protons are a thousand times bigger than quarks and leptons. An encounter between two quarks a million years ago could be important today.

Spin, a property of electrons and some nuclei, is now the source of much information. The mechanisms of energy exchange, structural variations, biological processes, diagnosis of pathological states by magnetic resonance imaging are all data based on electron or nuclear spin. Spin is related to time in such a way that by measuring so-called spin relaxation it is possible to observe Heisenberg's Uncertainty Principle[4] experimentally. The life of a spin at a certain energy level depends closely on relations, encounters and correlations with the surrounding environment. So much so, that the changing map of relaxation times in nuclear magnetic resonance experiments can tell us whether an anomalous process is occurring in a given tissue or organ or the blood.

Einstein, determinism and chance

The fascination of these physical experiments lies in the fact that small variations in a tiny building block of matter manifest themselves as large changes in biological processes. The paradox of modern scientific research in this field lies in the fact that the greater the detail in which we seek 'pure' mechanisms or given subparticles, the more confirmation we have of the validity of quantum mechanics and the more important information we have on the structure of matter. On the other hand, starting from elementary particles, the more we study interactions with biological systems and ecosystems, the more we discover the complexity, irreversibility and intrinsic aleatory character of nature. In chaos we rediscover the spontaneity of evolutionary history: a universe in which God plays dice, to invert Einstein's phrase.[5]

God was the supreme guarantee of physical determinism. For Einstein, protagonist of the first 'heroic' phase of quantum physics, physical

---

[4] This famous principle states that $\Delta q \times \Delta p \geq h/2\pi$ where Δq is the uncertainty in position, Δp the uncertainty in momentum (mass $\times$ velocity) and h Planck's constant, usually 6.626×10^{-34} joules per second.

determinism applied to any process. However, Max Born[6] once told Einstein that a deterministic universe was innately anathema to him. Born admitted that Einstein might be right, but added that determinism did not seem to hold in physics, much less in other fields. Born criticised Einstein's comment that God plays dice,[7] observing that Einstein's deterministic world needed chance. Born's wife Hedwig had previously written to their "dear friend Albert" that she could not admit a universal law according to which everything was predetermined, including whether or not she vaccinated her child against diphtheria.[8]

Lotus flowers

With complexity and irreversibility we discover the fascination of systemic biology and the intimate essences of relations and constraints. The biological complexity that we observe today in the natural world is the result of the temporal and spatial constraints of our planet and a long evolutionary history made up of relations accumulating in time. Different

---

[5] On 4th December 1926, Einstein wrote to Max Born that although quantum mechanics was worthy of respect, an inner voice told him that it was not yet the right solution, because it did not enable us to penetrate the secret of the Great Old Man, who he was sure did not play dice with the world (*Science and life*, Letters 1916-1955, letter no. 52 in A. Einstein, H. and M. Born). Max Born considered that there was a profound divergence of viewpoint between Einstein and the following generation, to which Born, though only a few years younger than Einstein, regarded himself as belonging. In a previous letter (29th April 1924, no. 48 of the above collection) Einstein observed that the ideas of Niels Bohr on radiation were interesting but he himself did not wish to be led away from rigorous causality. He added that he could not tolerate the idea that an electron exposed to radiation could freely choose when and in which direction to jump. Were this so, he said he would prefer to be a shoemaker or a gambler rather than a physicist. In his introduction to this collection of letters, Werner Heisenberg comments that Einstein agreed with Born on the fact that the mathematical formalism of quantum mechanics, which originated in Göttingen and was subsequently elaborated at Cambridge and Copenhagen, correctly represented the phenomena occurring inside the atom, but that he did not recognize quantum mechanics as a definitive or even exhaustive representation of these phenomena. The theme that God does NOT play dice recurs elsewhere in the Born-Einstein correspondence (e.g. Einstein's letters of 7th September 1944 and 12th October 1953, nos. 81 and 103, respectively).

[6] 10th October 1944 (letter no. 84 in *Science and life*).

[7] The expression "God plays dice" obviously had an irrational overtone for Einstein but, as we shall see, not for us.

[8] 9th October 1944 (letter no. 82 in *Science and life*).

hierarchies of biological complexity have marked different phases of the Earth's history: membranes with selective permeability and active transport of metabolites three billion years ago, differentiated systems of organs and tissues one billion years ago, the central nervous system 600 million years ago, warm blooded animals 150 million years ago, the first hominids three million years ago, the use of tools about 100,000 years ago.

The rules of the system of relations, the underlying hierarchy, the order in space and time and the correlations between time and forms all have still to be studied and understood. I agree with the optimistic view of Peacocke[9] that new concepts such as the quality factor of Manfred Eigen and the dissipative structures of Ilya Prigogine are the first steps towards an understanding of the principles regulating biological systems. I also agree with Peacocke that the ideas of physical chemistry: thermo-dynamics, kinetics and entropy, are the key to a new scientific world, a world of uncertainty and complexity, without paradigms, without hard edges, where quantity coexists with quality, the exact datum with the aleatory, reproducibility with unpredictable irreversibility, matter with time. In the following chapters I shall extend several global models of the biosphere along these lines.

In the previous chapters we have seen how biological systems of increasing complexity developed from photosynthesis; we have seen the role played by entropy in biological evolution; today we know that complexity and diversity functioned perfectly to maintain life for thousands of millions of years. Today a technological upstart who has existed for only two million years (a mere instant on the scale of biological time) presumes to play with ancient equilibria and to explain everything with simple mathematical equations. Luckily, in his genetic heritage there is also the wisdom of nature and respect for the sacred quality of nature. We need to listen, to recover the relationship of mind and nature, and to make appropriate choices in the fields of scientific research and socioeconomics. I shall deal with these questions in later chapters.

However I should like to emphasize that the greatest risk occurs when the biological clock is accelerated and biodiversity and the genetic heritage are destroyed. A magnolia leaf from 250,000 centuries ago, preserved, still green, on the floor of a frozen lake in Idaho, enabled us

---

[9] A.R. Peacocke, *The physical chemistry of biological organization*, Oxford Science Publications, Oxford, 1989.

to study an ancient genetic heritage. It was discovered that changes in the genetic code of the magnolia have been extremely slow, occurring at a rate of about one every million years. The slow biological clock must sometimes be put ahead and sometimes set back; in Pakistan a terrestrial whale was discovered from 50 million years ago, much earlier than they had been thought to exist. On the other hand, on an island in the Arctic Ocean, the discovery was made of fossilized remains of a mammoth, which was much closer to us in time than had previously been believed. It is thought to have inhabited Wrangel Island when the Egyptians were building the pyramids on the banks of the Nile.

Ecological archaeology may still have many exciting surprises. In 1951, three lotus seeds from about 2,000 years ago were found in a peat deposit near Tokyo. They were placed in water. One germinated four days later.

The lotus flower causes loss of memory,[10] but the genetic memory of its seed remains intact. At the crossroads ahead of us, one road, that of technological consumerism, leads into the maze of forgetfulness; the other, that of ecological responsibility, leads man back to his rightful place, with nature, in a common evolutionary history.

---

[10] Those of Ulysses's companions who ate the lotus flower had to be dragged back to the boats by force. Homer, *The Odyssey*, Book IX.

6

THE PLANET EARTH PLAYS DICE

Relations

Now we can look at some of the relations connecting the origin of life, biological evolution, entropy and the Earth.

a) The entropy of the universe is increasing (Second Law of Thermodynamics), whereas the entropy of the Earth has decreased in the course of evolution by dispersing positive entropy into space.

b) If we think of the evolution of a system in terms of statistical mechanics, we think of evolution towards more and more disordered states (Boltzmann's Theorem H) with high entropy values, whereas biological evolution moves towards more complex and ordered forms with low entropy values.

c) Living systems are driven by negentropy, made available directly or indirectly by photosynthesis.

d) The equilibrium state (immobility, non-differentiation, death) is characterized by an entropy maximum, whereas a system in the steady state (dynamicity, diversity, life) is maintained as far as possible from equilibrium by a flow of energy. The biosphere is a steady-state system.

e) Life originated on the basis of a metabolic capacity to extract negative entropy from the environment.

f) The Earth lives because of negentropy, not DNA. It cannot reproduce itself and its life is associated with stochastic and irreversible processes occurring in the biosphere. The Earth 'plays dice', because this is an intrinsic characteristic of biological evolution, the entropy function and the evolution of the energy-matter system.

Obviously, this game of dice obeys certain rules determined by the constraints of the planet and by its history. An event occurs in a stochastic manner because it is preceded by others. There are historical, genetic and environmental constraints. Evolutionary events proceed in a manner that depends on time: they show a direction of time; they are irreversible. Past time has determined the constraints; the future is largely unpredictable, and always has a stochastic or probable element.

The evolutionary process is such that systems become more and more complex and organized. Biological diversity is the product of long-term interactions at a genealogical and ecological level: the genealogical interactions relate to the dissipation of entropy by irreversible biological processes; the ecological interactions relate to entropy gradients in the environment.

Today we can almost answer, but only in an evolutionary and chemical context, two of the questions of Paul Gaugin's painting: Where do we come from? and What are we? We shall never be able to answer the third question: Where are we going? This does not mean that man cannot prevent (or procure) future catastrophes. An event may create complexity and order, decrease entropy, and increase information and biodiversity, or it may destroy all of this. When we play poker we do not know how the game will finish, but it would be idiotic to discard a pair of aces if we have four in our hand.

The role of thermodynamics in scientific thought boils down to defining relations and identifying constraints; thermodynamics is the science of what is possible and is to physics as logic is to philosophy. Entropy is the enigma of thermodynamics because it has the intrinsic properties of time irreversibility, quality and information that other thermodynamic functions lack. This is why entropy is a central concept in biology and ecology.

A special guest at Babette's feast[1]

Miss Entropy is invited to Babette's feast to celebrate the origin of life. It is a very special feast, for which resources have been spent in order to obtain maximum quality, maximum diversity of harmonizing tastes and maximum aesthetics and information. Energy has been poured in so that Miss Entropy is satisfied and shows that eccentric negative sign that means richness of quality, information and diversity. At the feast, proteins and nucleic acids meet, one essential for metabolism, the other for replication: two things necessary for life.

The questions discussed at Babette's feast are not trivial. A steam

---

[1] *Babette's feast*, a film by G. Axel from the short story by Karen Blixen.

engine can be studied in terms of thermal and mechanical energy and does not require very detailed knowledge of the state of the system. Moreover the system can be assumed to be constant in time, and the experiment is therefore reproducible. On the other hand, if we are dealing with a highly organized system, rich in systemic relations, far from equilibrium, evolving in time (such as a living cell), the details, time and relations become crucial, and with them, the role of information. As Harold Morowitz says, a methyl group in the wrong place can kill a whale. The entropy function and its relation to information, irrespective of the presence or absence of energy changes, now come into the picture.

In general, if a system goes from a higher to a lower entropy state, there is a gain in information. Entropy is proportional to a function that measures the lack of information on the microstate of the system. It is a maximum when all microstates have the same probability and cannot be distinguished. *Information is therefore equivalent to negentropy.* In the case of the mixing of a red and a yellow gas described in Chapter 1, we first have a low entropy situation and the exact information that the yellow molecule is in, let us say, the left container, and the red one in the right. After mixing we have two possible and equivalent states (the orange situation). Entropy increases and we no longer know whether the yellow molecule is on the right or on the left. Brillouin was right in stating that physical entropy is the information entropy of Shannon-Weaver with a change in sign.[2]

In biology, things are complicated by the difficulty of determining the microstate of a living organism without altering that state. The problem of the observer is different from the problem the system has of knowing its own microstate. A hypothetical external observer is in a different condition of knowledge from an observer that evolved together with the Earth; an indian knows the Amazon rainforest better than anyone else does. This is the difference between physical and biological research. The latter is not based on experiments to measure the position and motion of all the atoms comprising a living system, but solicits a group of cells in order to have a response to questions posed in the framework of the investigator's knowledge.

The relation between observer and system, and the consequent alterations, are described by Heisenberg's Uncertainty Principle. If I want

---

[2] This statement is derived from Brillouin's 'negentropy principle'. For more details see H. Dieter-Zeh, *The physical basis of the direction of time*, Springer-Verlag, Berlin, 1992, and H. Reichenbach, *The direction of time*, University of California Press, Berkeley, 1956.

to know the trajectory of a cannonball fired by Baron von Münchhausen's cannon, and its energy, without resorting to the Baron's fantastic ideas, I should place a series of paper hoops in the path of the cannonball, so that I can reconstruct the trajectory from the holes. The more hoops I place, the more information I shall have on the trajectory and the less the error; but the cannonball will reach its target with less energy, having wasted it in perforating the hoops. Hence my information on its energy will be imprecise and the error large. The opposite is true if I place only a few hoops.

Another note on the relation between entropy and information concerns genetics and evolution. Manfred Eigen recently stated that biological evolution is evolution of information, and that the difference between chemical and biological molecules lies in their information. Eigen, however, reduces the relation to problems of structure, geometry and space, without considering the role of the event in time; nucleic acid can reproduce a structure after meeting it, and, naturally, after formation of the structure. The creative role of entropy and time cannot be ignored.

Other entropy stories, with unicorns, cyclops and the return of Maxwell's devil

In his sixth memorandum to the Naturforschende Gesellschaft of Zurich,[3] Clausius wrote: "To express how much the molecules of a body are separate from each other, let us introduce a new quantity that we shall call the 'dissociation' of the body". Clausius rightly included this quantity in the entropy function. Nicholas Georgescu-Roegen,[4] on the other hand, proposed a 'Fourth Law of Thermodynamics' (a somewhat unfortunate term)[5] for the entropy of matter. We discussed it one afternoon several years ago at my home, in the presence of several economist and physicist friends. In the end, everyone stuck to his own opinion: Georgescu-Roegen convinced of his Fourth Law, I that everything can be traced back to the Second Law, with due respect to the practical importance of Georgescu-Roegen's intuition. The physical and mathematical aspect of the dispute was recently published by us in an article in *Ecological Economics*

---

[3] Rudolph Clausius, On the application of the theorem of the equivalence of transformation to internal work, in R. Clausius, *The mechanical theory of heat*, ed. T.A. Hirst, London 1867, 215-250 and in *Philosophical magazine*, **24**, 1862, 215-51.

[4] Nicholas Georgescu-Roegen, *The entropy law and the economic process*, Harvard University Press, Cambridge, MA, 1971; *Energy and economic myths*, Pergamon, New York, 1976.

(Complete recycling of matter in the frameworks of physics, biology and ecological economics).[6]

Georgescu-Roegen assumes the existence of an entropy of matter that tends to a maximum (maximum disorder and mixing of matter) such that in the end matter is no longer available. The Fourth Law states that it is impossible to completely recover matter involved in the production of mechanical work or dispersed by friction, irrespective of the quantity of energy and time expended on recovery. However, photosynthesis shows that this is not so, as witness the selective recovery of carbon dioxide molecules dispersed in the atmosphere by green plants using solar energy, or recovery of nitrogen dispersed by nitrogen-fixing bacteria in the roots of leguminous plants, or recovery of iron filings by electromagnetic energy. The law of Georgescu-Roegen is contained within the Second Law. The point is that to recover dispersed matter a passage from ordered forms of energy (mechanical, electromagnetic, chemical) to less ordered forms of energy (heat) is required. The rubber worn from tyres or the

---

[5] I am not satisfied with the 'Fourth Law' for the following reasons. The first principle (rather than law) of thermodynamics is the principle of conservation of energy for thermodynamic systems. It can substantially be ascribed to J.R. Mayer (1842) and J.P. Joule (1840, 1849). Formulated more specifically, it says that if a system is subjected to a cyclic transformation (returning in the end to its initial state), the work done by the system is proportional to the quantity of heat absorbed (the proportionality constant is the so-called thermal equivalent of work). If on the other hand the system undergoes a change in state (usually defined in terms of volume, pressure and temperature), the difference between the heat absorbed and the work done is equal to the change in internal energy. In 1852, William Thomson (Lord Kelvin) formulated the second principle as the impossibility of a change, the sole result of which is a transformation of heat, obtained from a constant temperature source, into work. The principle is equivalent to the so-called Clausius proposition, according to which if heat flows by conduction from a hotter body A to a colder body B, it is impossible to carry out a transformation which has the sole result of making heat flow from B to A. In terms of the state function known as entropy, the second principle reads: for any transformation in an isolated system, the entropy of the final state can never be less than that of the initial state. Entropy is defined by a formula with an additive constant which is eliminated by the so-called Nernst theorem. This is the proposition formulated by W. Nernst in 1907, and sometimes called the Third Law or principle of thermodynamics, according to which entropy is zero at zero absolute temperature. This can also be worded as the impossiblity of reaching zero absolute. For the plausibility of the Nernst proposition, see E. Fermi, *Thermodynamics*, first ed. 1958, second ed. 1972 and subsequent editions, Boringhieri, Turin.

[6] C. Bianciardi, E. Tiezzi, S. Ulgiati, Complete recycling of matter in the frameworks of physics, biology and ecological economics, *Ecological economics*, **8**, 1993, 1-5.

metal worn from coins can be recovered only at the cost of a great increase in entropy in the surrounding environment (and enormous economic expenditure). In other words, complete recycling of matter is physically possible if a sufficient quantity of energy is available. The problem is that such a waste of energy would lead to a tremendous, certainly non-sustainable increase in the entropy of the biosphere.

Essentially, Georgescu-Roegen (not his Fourth Law) is right. As Maxwell's devil can exist only in an imaginary universe, so the recovery of dispersed particles of matter could occur only with the intervention of unicorns and cyclops.

> Unicorns and cyclops,
> golden horns
> and green eyes.
> On the rocks,
> in gigantic throngs,
> clean mercury
> without crystal from the sea.[7]

My book falls to the ground

I am convinced of the stochastic character of life, that is, of the simultaneous and necessary roles of choice and chance. The choice between various possibilities and random encounters with the environment determine natural evolution and the bursting in of time upon biology. An event, an encounter, a collision between particles, a choice, determine what happens later; this is the meaning of the concept of entropy and the arrow of time.

Mario Ageno[8] speaks, appropriately, of the 'historical character of biology', underlining the personalization of fundamental particles, the genes of a microbe: personalization at the basis of biological variability and the continuous appearance of new types. Ageno adds that this historical character does not contradict the laws of physics and chemistry, but that these laws are unable to dominate it. This is the eternal dilemma

---

[7] F. Garcia Lorca, *Collected poems (Tutte de poesie)*, translated by Carlo Bo, Garzanti, Milan, 1980, 352-353.

[8] M. Ageno, *Le origini della irreversibilità*, Bollati Boringhieri, Turin, 1992; see also M. Ageno, *Dal non vivente al vivente*, Theoria, Rome, 1991, and M. Ageno, *Punti cardinali*, Sperling and Kupfer, Milan, 1992.

between the legality of physics and the historical character of biology, between determinism and evolution.

Let us now try to think of an inanimate object in historical terms. My book falls to the ground and some pages come out. The potential energy is converted to thermal energy which is dissipated in the ground, increasing the entropy of the ground. The book is at a lower potential energy than before. Since E is a function of state, the book is in an energy state E_2 where $E_2 < E_1$.

Some pages of the book have come out. Page 3 is no longer in its right place, but could now be in any of a hundred places, since the book has one hundred pages. There is a loss of information as regards the position of page 3; initially there was one possible state, now there are a hundred. According to Brillouin there has been an increase in entropy.

The book is in a disordered state. If it were written in Etruscan and the pages were not numbered and an archaeologist found it, the amount of information that he would obtain would be much less than the amount available when the book was in its initial ordered state:

$$S_2 > S_1.$$

The environment (ground) and the system (the book) have both had an increase in entropy, but there has also been an increase in energy for the ground. For the book there has certainly been an overall decrease in energy, even if it got back some thermal energy when it hit the ground.

An energy flow can lead to destruction (increase in entropy, for example a cannon ball) or organization (decrease in entropy, for example photosynthesis). The same quantity of energy can destroy a wall or kill a man; obviously the loss of information and negentropy is much greater in the second case. Energy and information are never equivalent.

The classical example of the mixing of gases in an isolated system shows us that there can be an increase in entropy without energy input from outside. The point is that E and S are both functions of state, but energy is intrinsically reversible whereas entropy is not. Entropy has the broken time symmetry of which Prigogine speaks. In other words, entropy has an energy term plus a time term that energy does not have. The entropy of the ground has increased only due to a quantity of dissipated thermal energy, whereas the entropy of the book or the gases has increased due to an event. Entropy has an intrinsic temporal parameter. Energy obeys spatial and material constraints; entropy obeys spatial, material and temporal constraints.

The time term, which is also linked to the quantity of information, does not prevent entropy from being a function of state. Intrinsic time,[9] unlike a time interval, is a function of state. Entropy breaks the symmetry of time. Entropy can change (state S_2 is different from S_1), irrespective of changes in energy, with mere changes in time, with events. S_2 is a function of s_2 and t_2; S_1 is a function of s_1 and t_1. That is, S_2 is a function of spatial (s_2) and temporal (t_1) coordinates, as is S_1.

If history and the succession of events are of scientific relevance, the concept of function of state should be revised at a higher level of complexity. The singularity of an event also becomes of particular importance; if a certain quantity of energy is spent to kill a caterpillar, we lose the information embodied in the caterpillar. But were this the last caterpillar, we should lose its unique genetic information forever. The last caterpillar is different from the nth caterpillar.

Stories take place in a setting, the details of which are not irrelevant to the story. What happens in the biosphere, the story of life, depends on the constraints of the biosphere itself. Hence it is important to have global models of the biosphere in terms of space, time, matter, energy, entropy and information, and their respective relations.

The thermodynamics of Prigogine

When observing life in nature, one is bewildered by its complexity. After millennia of human curiosity and centuries of systematic research, we are still far from understanding how this complicated system was established and how it is maintained.

In 1859, Charles Darwin wrote *The origin of species*, presenting a new evolutionary paradigm. In the same period, Clausius formulated the Second Law of Thermodynamics. If Darwin tells us that evolution increases the organization of life, how can this be reconciled with the Clausius theory which claims that disorder accompanies the increasing complexity of nature? This contradiction has been magnificently overcome by Ilya Prigogine,[10] who observed that non-equilibrium can be a source of order. In fact, irreversible processes may lead to a new type of dynamic state of matter called 'dissipative structures'. These manifest

---

[9] This parameter is related to the 'internal time' and 'natural time ordering' of Prigogine and to the concept of the arrow of time.

[10] I. Prigogine, Introduction to thermodynamics of irreversible processes, C.C. Thomas, Springfield, 1954.

a coherent, supermolecular character which leads to new, quite spectacular manifestations, such as biochemical cycles involving oscillatory enzymes. These spatio-temporal structures arise from the non-linear dynamics of such phenomena. How do such coherent structures appear as the result of reactive collisions? Can thermodynamics give us an answer?

The classical thermodynamics of Clausius refers to isolated systems exchanging neither energy nor matter with the outside world. The Second Law then merely ascertains the existence of a function S, which increases monotonically to a maximum at the state of thermodynamic equilibrium:

$$dS/dt \geq 0.$$

This formulation can be extended to systems which exchange energy and matter with the outside world, in which case it is necessary to distinguish two terms in the entropy change dS: the first, $d_e S$, is the transfer of entropy across the boundaries of the system; the second, $d_i S$, is the entropy produced within the system by irreversible processes:

$$dS = d_i S + d_e S \qquad\qquad d_i S \geq 0.$$

In this formulation, the distinction between irreversible and reversible processes is essential. Only irreversible processes produce entropy. The Second Principle therefore states that irreversible processes lead to a sort of unidirectional time. For isolated systems $d_e S = 0$ and the previous equation becomes the classical Second Law. Open systems could conceivably evolve to steady states with:

$$d_e S = - d_i S \qquad\qquad dS = 0.$$

This is a non-equilibrium steady state that should not be confused with thermodynamic equilibrium, and in which order may be created from disorder. Order created in this way no longer violates the laws of thermodynamics; equilibrium is no longer the only attractor of the system, but the world becomes more complex and thermodynamics can embrace new worlds characterized by highly organized as well as chaotic structures.

The simplest example of a self-organizing system is the Bénard instability. A thin layer of liquid is kept with its lower surface heated and its upper surface at room temperature. For a small temperature difference close to equilibrium, heat is transferred only by conduction, that is, through intermolecular collisions. Above a certain temperature gradient, the heat is also transferred by convection. This means that the molecules participate in collective motions in the form of vortices dividing the layer into regular cells. If we further increase the temperature difference, the motion becomes less regular and we have a transition to turbulence and spatio-temporal chaos.

Far from equilibrium, we witness new states of matter having properties sharply at variance with those of equilibrium states. This suggests that irreversibility plays a fundamental role in nature. We must therefore introduce the foundations of irreversibility into our basic description of nature.

7

WHAT A FUNNY PLANET!

*"La terre est comme une orange bleue
on en retrouve encore
sur la planète
de ces vieux sycomores.
Abandonnés par la mer
sur la plage,
sont récoltés par les poètes,
encore si sauvages,
ces oxymores."*

Paul Éluard

Towards an ecodynamic model

What a funny planet, this blue orange! We have seen that it is a most singular planet, characterized as it is by a decrease in entropy, unlike the rest of the universe. An ecological model of our planet must take this peculiarity into account.

We also have to consider that small changes in one place may cause chain reactions, non-linear effects and even environmental disasters distant in space and time, and unforeseeable. Deterministic models based on the principles of mechanics cannot predict ecological phenomena. The thermodynamics of biological systems and evolutionary studies reveal the role of time, no longer an aseptic, reversible, external parameter. The view of the world as a machine is inadequate for the new science of ecology.

"By definition, a model is something that needs no changes, that works perfectly, whereas reality clearly does not work and is falling to pieces.

---

[1] I. Calvino, *Palomar*, Einaudi, Turin, 1983; the quotation is from "Il modello dei modelli" (The model of models), our translation.

The only solution is somehow to force it to fit the model."[1]

Palomar, in Italo Calvino's novel, observes that if a model fails to describe reality, then the solution is to force reality to fit the model. If we decide to resort to the paradoxical solution of Mr. Palomar, we need a change of paradigm whenever the divergence between theory and reality become too large, as underlined by Thomas Kuhn.[2]

In this chapter we try to create a new ecodynamic model, shifting the 'gestalt' from being to evolving and from the energy function to the entropy function, understood as the intrinsic property of matter and energy, not only in a quantitative but also in a qualitative, information and temporal sense. In other words, entropy seen as the natural trend of things, 'clinamen', to use a beautiful Lucretian term.

The model is concerned with interactions between biophysical constraints and the global environment. The epistemological bases of the model are derived from the mixing of environmental physical chemistry (mainly thermodynamics) with systemic ecology. The starting point is Boltzmann's statement, reported in Chapter 2, that the struggle for life is not the struggle for matter and energy, which are substantially constant in time, but the struggle for negative entropy supplied by the sun.

In other words, the model underlines the peculiar capacity of the biosphere to decrease the entropy of the planet by capturing solar energy. This is done by photosynthesis, in the broad sense of 'making things with light', storing energy in the organization of living organisms and decreasing the entropy of the biosphere with the help of radiation from an external source. We have seen that these statements are summarized in Schrödinger's phrase that life feeds on negative entropy. Negative entropy is therefore taken as a precondition for life, and biological evolution, in turn, can be read as the history of negative entropy on the Earth.

This type of model is described by the word 'ecodynamic'. For spatial coordinates, the biosphere is defined as the geometric locus in which entropy decreases, or as the geometric locus of photosynthesis. Within this space, time modulates structures and forms by virtue of negative entropy stored as information. The biosphere is in a steady state; it does not grow quantitatively but only in biodiversity (or at least it has grown in biodiversity from the origin of life until fairly recently). Since the exchange of matter with the outside is practically negligible and, on the other hand, the Earth receives an enormous flux of energy from outside,

---

[2] T.S. Kuhn, *The structure of scientific revolutions*, University of Chicago Press, Chicago, 1962.

the biosphere can be regarded as a closed thermodynamic system. This means that matter cannot leave (this is why wastes are such a problem today) or be exchanged, whereas energy is exchanged with the rest of the universe by virtue of the existence of a source (the sun) and a sink (celestial space). In this closed system, the negative entropy flux permits the creation of dissipative structures, complexity, new information, biodiversity (even cultural diversity) and relations stored in the energy-matter system. The closed system biosphere is composed of a multitude of open systems: living organisms.

As we have seen, the *conditio sine qua non* for all this to continue is the absence of an adiabatic membrane around the planet. In other words, the increased greenhouse effect must not be allowed to prevent the flow of positive entropy into space.

The role of carbon dioxide and other 'greenhouse' gases becomes determinant in this ecodynamic model, one reason being the great difference between the biological time required for the formation of fossil fuels and the fleeting historical time in which the fossil fuels are being used. This is why the model regards fossil deposits (oil and coal) as external to the space of the biosphere, as we have defined it. The bags in which the fossils are stored are regarded as external to the closed system. The space of the biosphere is defined as the spherical corona of the planet including the atmosphere and the ozonosphere, the oceans and the Earth's crust, but not reduced carbon which has effectively been treated as a waste by nature, and relegated to the bowels of the Earth, the biological dustbin.

If we examine the spatial model in more detail, we find that the boundary between the biosphere and the universe is open to the entry of flows of energy and matter. It receives more than 10^{24} joules per year of solar energy, an enormous quantity, and receives practically no matter, with the exception of meteorites and atmospheric dust, a negligible quantity in relation to the mass of the planet.

The same boundary is not open to the exit of flows of matter (with the negligible exception of space vehicles) because of gravitation, but is open to the exit of an enormous flow of degraded energy (positive entropy), the necessary condition for the maintenance of life and for negative entropy. Man can alter this situation by dumping greenhouse gases into the atmosphere. This is why the increase in carbon dioxide touches a vital ganglion of our planet, and is a critical change from the ecological point of view.

The boundary between the spherical corona and the centre of the Earth is open to outward flows of matter (minerals, fossils) and energy (geothermal energy). It is not open to the inward flow of energy because of the higher temperature of the centre of the Earth. In the past this compartment received enormous quantities of matter (reduced carbon produced by primordial photosynthesis).

We have described a typical ecodynamic model, the protagonists of which are the carbon cycle, photosynthesis, energy flows and entropy. It is like a beautiful intricate antique toy in the hands of a spoilt child, the human consumer of today. In order to have a good understanding of the cultural traits of this improvident consumerism and why we find ourselves in the present decadence, let us take a step backwards...

Like the face of the Moon

The ravages committed by man subvert the relations and destroy the balance which nature had established between her organized and her inorganic creations, and she avenges herself upon the intruder, by letting loose upon her defaced provinces destructive energies hitherto kept in check by organic forces destined to be his best auxiliaries, but which he has unwisely dispersed and driven from the field of action. When the forest is gone, the great reservoir of moisture stored up in its vegetable mould is evaporated, and returns only in deluges of rain to wash away the parched dust into which that mould has been converted. The well-wooded and humid hills are turned to ridges of dry rock, which encumbers the low grounds and chokes the watercourses with its debris, and – except in countries favoured with an equable distribution of rain through the seasons, and a moderate and regular inclination of surface – the whole Earth, unless rescued by human art from the physical degradation to which it tends, becomes an assemblage of bald mountains, of barren, turfless hills, and of swampy and malarious plains. There are parts of Asia Minor, of Northern Africa, of Greece, and even of Alpine Europe, where the operation of causes set in action by man has brought the face of the Earth to a desolation almost as complete as that of the moon; and though, within that brief space of time which we call 'the historical period', they are known to have been covered with luxuriant woods, verdant pastures, and fertile meadows, they are now too far deteriorated to be reclaimable by man, nor can they become again fitted for human use, except through great geological changes, or other mysterious influences or agencies of which we have no present knowledge, and over which we have no prospective control.[3]

This impressive scenario is taken from the pages of the masterpiece of George Perkins Marsh (1801-1882), erudite adventurer, red republican and critic of black slavery, unionist and collaborator of Abraham Lincoln. He personally saw the effects of 'progress' in the American west, and also in the Mediterranean basin, in Egypt, in the so-called Middle East and in the countries of industrialized Europe. With this experience he arrived in Italy in 1861, the first Ambassador of the United States of America to the new Kingdom of Italy. It was here that he wrote *Man and nature* which was to be published in 1864. In the preface, dated 1st December 1863, Marsh declared that the aim of his extensive research was to indicate the nature and extent of the changes caused by man to physical conditions on the globe we inhabit. In the preface to the Italian edition published by G. Barbera, Florence, in January 1870, he was even more pessimistic about the destructive effects of human activity.

Was Marsh an 'apocalyptic' among enthusiasts of the more ingenuous forms of positivity for human technical potential? We shall see. First of all, Marsh did not deny that the power to modify the environment was a trait common to man, animals and even plants, but he claimed that the difference in degree was almost infinite. Woodsmen and beavers both fell trees, but the former do it to convert forests into olive groves that will not produce for several generations; beavers do so to feed on the bark and for materials to build their dams. The wild animal acts on the basis of a primary direct need. The action of man, though often followed by unexpected and undesirable effects, is guided by a will which is intelligent and self-aware, and often aspires to secondary or remote aims.

This peculiarity of the influence of man on the environment is not unrelated to the breadth and irreversibility of the effects of 'civilized' man.

---

[3] G.P. Marsh, *Man and nature*, Scrivener, New York, 1864, pp. 49-50.

The wandering savage grows no cultivated vegetable, fells no
forest, and extirpates no useful plant, no noxious weed. If his
skill in the chase enables him to entrap numbers of the animals
on which he feeds, he compensates this loss by destroying also
the lion, the tiger, the wolf, the otter, the seal, and the eagle,
thus indirectly protecting the feebler quadrupeds and fish and
fowls, which would otherwise become the booty of beasts and
birds of prey.

With the stationary life style of the herder and farmer, things changed
radically:

...man at once commences an almost indiscriminate warfare
upon all the forms of animal and vegetable existence around
him, and as he advances in civilization, he gradually eradicates
or transforms every spontaneous product of the soil he
occupies.

Is this the price of progress? It may well be; what I want to underline,
however, is that in the framework of the relationship between man and
the environment, human 'influence' involves a loss of biological diversity.
This was clearly expounded by Marsh, and in so doing he anticipated
ecology.[4]

Man (...) extends his action over vast spaces, his revolutions are
swift and radical, and his devastations are, for an almost
incalculable time after he has withdrawn the arm that gave the
blow, irreparable.

Is it really possible to withdraw the arm? With unusual foresight, Marsh
understood that devastation of the environment (and hence the
resources not only of the agents and their children but also other
inhabitants of the planet, remote in space and time) could be ascribed to
the free and easy ruling classes of countries that today we would call
'developing'. Among these countries, Marsh included Italy, which at the
time was making the transition from an agricultural to an industrial
economy.

But changes like these must await not only great political and
moral revolutions in the governments and peoples by whom
those regions are now possessed, but, especially, a command
of pecuniary and of mechanical means not at present enjoyed

---

[4] The study of what Lamarck called *monde ambient* becomes genuine ecology in the
approach of Ernst Haeckel (1834-1919). The work of Marsh makes him a pioneer of
contemporary scientific thought.

by those nations, and a more advanced and generally diffused knowledge of the processes by which the amelioration of soil and climate is possible than now anywhere exists.

Nature's revenge

In *Man and Nature*, Marsh dedicates many pages to the perverse relationship between devastation and 'civilization'. These pages illustrate what in my opinion should be the nucleus of any policy of sustainable development, namely that historical or human time is not the same as biological or natural time. Marsh examines the thoughtless impetus with which 'emancipated' peoples destroy forests. This is done in the name of Safety, Civilization, Equality and so forth. With the first forms of national state in Europe, forests offering refuge to bandits and various illegalities were destroyed. With the French Revolution, not only the Bastille fell, but the 'people of France' tore down the palisades and barriers that protected the forests, which were the exclusive hunting ground of the hated aristocrats. The American free settlers did not spare animals or plants in their wars of extermination of the indigenous Indian tribes.[5] The present systematic clearing of the Amazon rainforests has more than one precedent.

With the extirpation of the forest, all is changed. At one season, the Earth parts with its warmth by radiation to an open sky – receives, at another, an immoderate heat from the unobstructed rays of the sun. Hence the climate becomes excessive, and the soil is alternately parched by the fervors of summer, and seared by the rigors of winter. Bleak winds sweep unresisted over its surface, drift away the snow that sheltered it from the frost, and dry up its scanty moisture. The precipitation becomes as irregular as the temperature; the melting snows and vernal rains, no longer absorbed by a loose and bibulous vegetable mould, rush over the frozen surface, and pour down the valleys seawards, instead of filling a retentive bed of absorbent earth, and storing up a supply of moisture to feed perennial springs. The soil is bared of its covering of leaves, broken and loosened by the plough,

---

[5] These concepts and the following long quotation are from Chap. III of *Man and nature*, perhaps the culminating point of Marsh's work.

deprived of the fibrous rootlets which held it together, dried
and pulverized by sun and wind, and at last exhausted by new
combinations. The face of the earth is no longer a sponge, but
a dust-heap, and the floods which the waters of the sky pour
over it hurry swiftly along its slopes, carrying in suspension vast
quantities of earthy particles which increase the abrading
power and mechanical force of the current, and, augmented by
the sand and gravel of falling banks, fill the beds of the
streams, divert them into new channels, and obstruct their
outlets. The rivulets, wanting their former regularity of supply
and deprived of the protecting shade of the woods, are heated,
evaporated, and thus reduced in their summer currents, but
swollen to raging torrents in autumn and spring. From these
causes, there is a constant degradation of the uplands, and a
consequent elevation of the beds of water-courses and of lakes
by the deposition of the mineral and vegetable matter carried
down by the waters. The channels of great rivers become
unnavigable, their estuaries are choked up, and harbors which
once sheltered large navies are shoaled by dangerous sand-bars.
The earth, stripped of its vegetable glebe, grows less and less
productive, and, consequently, less able to protect itself by
weaving a new network of roots to bind its particles together,
a new carpeting of turf to shield it from wind and sun and
scouring rain. Gradually it becomes altogether barren. The
washing of the soil from the mountains leaves bare ridges of
sterile rock, and the rich organic mould which covered them,
now swept down into the dank low grounds, promotes a
luxuriance of aquatic vegetation that breeds fever, and more
insidious forms of mortal disease, by its decay, and thus the
earth is rendered no longer fit for the habitation of man.

This dismal picture of floods, landslides, degradation of the landscape
and silting of water courses is the result of 'merciless sacking of the
forest heritage'. These genuine catastrophes are not acts of a malignant
and capricious Nature, but the products of imbalances wrought by *homo
faber*. In the terminology of this and other of my books, they are the
consequences of the difference between the time of human history and
the human economy, and the rhythms of the biosphere. Marsh was
convinced that trees and their products acted as absorbers, radiators,

reflectors and conductors of heat. By preventing transmission of heat they mitigated extremes and smoothed the temperature curve; he predicted a type of *ante litteram* greenhouse effect as one of the more hypothetical consequences of deforestation. He reasoned that the forests prevent the Sun's rays from reaching the ground and hence they also prevent the rise in temperature that would lead to increased evaporation. He considered that a few statistical observations were sufficient for a tentative conclusion that the mean temperature of deforested land in the tropics was about a Centigrade degree higher than that of forest. In 1864 (more than a century ago!) Marsh recognized the paradox that mankind's influence on natural scenarios, driven by the aim of maximum welfare for itself, was dangerous for humanity as a whole:

> The earth is fast becoming an unfit home for its noblest inhabitant, and another era of equal human crime and human improvidence, and of like duration with that through which traces of that crime and that improvidence extend, would reduce it to such a condition of impoverished productiveness, of shattered surface, of climatic excess, as to threaten the depravation, barbarism, and perhaps even extinction of the species.

Does mankind therefore risk erasing life from the planet Earth? After this glance at our recent past as 'pioneers' and 'devastators', let us return to our present.

The fragile equilibria of the atmosphere

As we saw in Chapter 3, one of the secrets of life lies in the capacity of the planet to radiate heat received from the sun back into space. This exchange is possible because of the penetrable nature of the terrestrial atmosphere. The increased greenhouse effect is making our atmosphere opaque to thermal radiation, upsetting equilibria which have existed for millions of years.

Like biological equilibria, the chemical equilibria of the various layers of the atmosphere are extremely sensitive to changes.[6] Sudden changes caused by man can lead to irreversible effects and chain reactions that can

---

[6] For the theory underlying this statement see Chapter 11. For the general subject of sudden changes in climate, the reader is referred to the interesting article by Wallace S. Broecker, "Chaotic climate", *Science,* **56**, 329, Jan 1996.

no longer be controlled. For instance, large-scale clearing of tropical rainforest and combustion of increasing quantities of fossil fuels affect these equilibria. Fossil fuels took millions of years to form and a large proportion of them have been burned over the period of two generations. As we saw in Chapter 2, the concentration of carbon dioxide in the Earth's atmosphere has increased in less than fifty years.

This increase affects the climate and agriculture, and leads to the melting of polar ice and the spread of deserts. If present trends in fossil fuel consumption continue, the quantity of carbon dioxide in the atmosphere will double in about fifty years. Scientists predict that such an increase will produce an increased greenhouse effect, with a significant increase in the temperature of the Earth. The temperature difference could be of the same order of magnitude as those separating the various geological eras, which would upset the already precarious ecological equilibria of the planet and damage world food production.[7]

Carbon dioxide build-up poses an unusual political problem. Human societies developed in a period of practically absolute climatic stability. This is no longer true, and the problem of carbon dioxide has always been linked to consumption of the planet's energy reserves. The stakes are high and the uncertainties many.

Every ton of coal burned produces three tons of carbon dioxide. In twenty-two years the carbon dioxide in the atmosphere has increased by 20 ppm, equivalent to 42 billion tons of coal. From the industrial revolution to today it is calculated that the carbon added to the atmosphere has been 85 billion tons, when the total quantity of carbon in the atmosphere is only 700 billion tons. B. Bolin of Stockholm University, world expert on land biota and the carbon cycle, writes that man has unwittingly triggered a global geochemical and climatic experiment that could easily get out of control; the sorcerer's apprentice does experiments on himself without knowing how to stop the process.[8]

The effects can already be felt, ranging from desertification in various parts of the world, to increased evaporation and consequent flash floods, and a decrease in size of the polar ice-caps. A new island can be drawn on the atlas: the hitherto Ross peninsula of Antarctica is now circumnavigable due to the detachment of an iceberg the size of Switzerland.

---

[7] See for example M. Gribbin and J. Gribbin, *Too hot to handle? The greenhouse effect*, Corgi Books, London, 1992, especially Chap. 1.

[8] B. Bolin, Changes of land biota and their importance for the carbon cycle, *Science*, **196**, 1977, 613-615.

The climatic importance of a gas such as carbon dioxide, present in traces (0.03%) in the atmosphere, is due to the fact that it absorbs radiation in a band of frequencies to which the other atmospheric gases are transparent. In other words, the heat emitted by the Earth which would pass through the atmosphere and be dispersed in space, is trapped by carbon dioxide.

The Sun emits a spectrum of frequencies: ultraviolet, visible, infrared, some of which are partially absorbed, diffused or reflected by the atmosphere. Clouds can reflect up to 70% of the total incident radiation, according to their altitude and thickness. The part of the radiant energy absorbed by the atmosphere is added to the global thermal content of the atmosphere and heats the Earth's surface.

The global temperature of the planet can remain constant only if the Earth and the atmosphere disperse the same quantity of energy as they absorb from the Sun, as underlined in the opening chapters (Morowitz model). The crucial point is that the Earth and the atmosphere can only disperse energy into space by emitting in the infrared band, but the frequency of the outgoing infrared energy is different from that of the solar radiation coming in. This is why carbon dioxide and water vapour do not absorb incoming but only outgoing radiation. Increasing concentrations of these gases in the atmosphere absorb increasing quantities of infrared energy. The energy absorbed is radiated back to Earth, increasing the total flux of radiant energy on the Earth's surface. This is the process known as the greenhouse effect.

It has been estimated that the Earth's surface would be 30-40°C colder without this additional energy flux. The surface of Mars is at -50°C because of the rarefaction of its atmosphere, whereas the surface of Venus, the atmosphere of which contains an abundance of carbon dioxide, is at more than 400°C, as we saw in Chapter 2. The increase of atmospheric carbon dioxide and greenhouse gases in general leads to an increase in absorption of infrared energy which is radiated back to Earth, leading to an increase in the temperature of the Earth's surface.

Unpredictable scenarios

The temperature of the surface of the primordial Earth was only 20-30°C less than it is now, though the Sun seems to have been 50 per cent less luminous than it is now. This is considered to be due to the stronger greenhouse effect associated with higher atmospheric concentrations of carbon dioxide produced by volcanic activity. Levels of this gas were probably higher before organisms capable of photosynthesis evolved and before carbonate deposition. Thousands of millions of years ago, much atmospheric carbon dioxide was converted into sedimentary deposits and fossils; coal, oil and methane are fossil residues of living organisms that fixed carbon dioxide by photosynthesis. Since then the Earth's climate has undergone large fluctuations. Ice ages have alternated with interglacial periods every 100,000 years or so. We are currently at about the middle of a relatively warm interglacial period that has lasted about 10,000 years. During these large climatic fluctuations, the sea level changed significantly, and temperature and precipitations moulded life. These changes, however, occurred in biological time (over many thousands of years) and evolution followed the modified environment at the same slow pace.

Changes in the mean temperature of the Earth's surface, deduced from palaeoclimatic data, were always very small (less than 0.1°C per decade) and the mean temperature drop during the 'little ice age' (1550-1850) is estimated to have been less than 1°C. With respect to these great but extremely slow climatic fluctuations, the impact of the rapid consumption of fossil fuels could be dangerous and complicated to predict. Opinions on the subject range from the complacent attitude that nature can buffer the damage caused by human activity, to the ingenuous belief that technology can repair the imbalances created. However, even historical analysis is subject to uncertainties in interpretation. An example is the question of the desertion of Mesa Verde villages, especially the Kayenta settlement in the Betatakin canyon in Arizona, attributed by some to a climatic variation characterized by a long period of drought. Others consider that the villages were abandoned because of soil erosion due to agriculture and irresponsible deforestation. This extraordinary ruin and the sudden southward migration of the Kayenta to the Hopi mountains remain a mystery.

The problem of carbon dioxide was already understood by eminent scientists last century: in 1827 Jean-Baptiste Fourier compared the atmosphere to a glass panel; in 1861 John Tyndall spoke of the role of this gas and the greenhouse effect; in 1896 Svante Arrhenius estimated that doubling of the atmospheric concentration of carbon dioxide would cause global warming of about 6°C. Today few climatologists doubt that human activity can affect global biophysical equilibria.

Until ten years ago, however, certain scientists minimized the problem, claiming that the ocean had the capacity to absorb all the carbon dioxide produced industrially. This opinion was subsequently disproved by two fundamental studies. Hans Seuss and Roger Revelle showed experimentally that the ocean depths absorb carbon dioxide extremely slowly, and calculated that up to 80 per cent of the carbon dioxide of industrial origin accumulates in the atmosphere. Even with a drastic decrease in carbon dioxide emissions it will not be possible to restore the 'pre-carbon-dioxide' situation and block the negative effects for more than several hundred years. The second study was based on the installation of high-precision detectors of carbon dioxide on Mauna Loa in Hawaii and at the US bases in Antarctica. This research showed an exponential[9] increase in atmospheric carbon dioxide.

Analysis of Antarctic ice cores by French and Swiss researchers has shown that carbon dioxide levels were about 260 ppm before the industrial revolution. This discovery lowers the hitherto accepted basal level, suggesting that the recent atmospheric build-up of this gas took place faster than was thought. Recent research and measurements carried out throughout the world confirm the increase in atmospheric concentrations of carbon dioxide, with higher values in the northern hemisphere, near the countries with the heaviest consumption of fossil fuels. Increased use of fossil fuels by industrialized and developing countries is predicted in the next 50 years, with grave consequences for global biophysical equilibrium. If the trend recorded on Mauna Loa continues, carbon dioxide concentrations could double before 2030: an infinitesimal interval on the biological time scale!

According to Enrico C. Lorenzini of the Harvard-Smithsonian Center for Astrophysics, the present composition of the atmosphere is the result of interaction with the biosphere during geological and biological evolution. For example, oxygen appeared in the atmosphere in the last billion years. The present atmospheric composition was largely determined by the advent of photosynthesis which decreased primordial carbon dioxide levels and increased those of oxygen.

Lorenzini maintains that carbon dioxide, methane, water vapour and other minor gases that trap infrared radiation reflected from the Earth's

---

[9] For the notion of exponential increase see footnote 14, Chap. 11.

surface enable the Earth to have a mean global surface temperature of about 15°C. If the atmosphere did not contain these 'greenhouse' gases, the mean global surface temperature would be only -18°C, hardly congenial for the living species of today. The greenhouse effect therefore contributes as much as 33°C to the present mean temperature of the Earth.

On the role of carbon dioxide in the history of biological evolution, Lorenzini explains that with the industrial revolution and the advent of motor transport, the interaction between man and the atmosphere changed substantially. Carbon dioxide and sulphur dioxide were discharged into the air from the combustion of fossil fuels, together with chemical substances such as chlorofluorocarbons (CFCs) used in refrigeration and air conditioning plants. This gave rise to three main worldwide environmental problems: (i) acid rain due to sulphur dioxide produced mainly by coal combustion, (ii) the decrease in stratospheric ozone due to atmospheric release of CFCs, (iii) warming of the troposphere due to increasing atmospheric concentrations of carbon dioxide, methane and other minor gases. The mean surface temperature of the Earth has increased by almost 0.5°C during the last century; in the same period, atmospheric carbon dioxide concentrations have increased by about 20%, from 300 to 350 ppm and the concentration of methane by almost 100%. It is certain that the increased percentage of these gases contributes to the rise in temperature; the repartition between man-made and natural contributions is less certain. Warming exists and continues, but its future trend will also be determined by atmospheric water vapour and by changes in cloud formation processes, both due to natural interactions between the atmosphere and the oceans, but also influenced by the increased greenhouse effect.

Lorenzini points out that carbon dioxide is directly linked to energy production from fossil fuels, and as such cannot be eliminated without eliminating these fuels. Sulphur dioxide and CFCs, on the other hand, can be excluded without major sacrifice. The unequivocal statement that fossil fuels are not a sustainable energy source has also frequently been underlined by US economist Herman Daly, at the World Bank.

Hence we have the certainty of the risk due to the increased greenhouse effect on the one hand and uncertainties about future scenarios on the other. Lorenzini continues that the most recent estimate of the future increase in mean global surface temperature is between 1°

and 4°C before the year 2100, on the basis of current projections of a doubling of atmospheric carbon dioxide concentrations in the same period. The most probable mean value is therefore an increase of around 2.5°C in about 100 years. To understand what an increase of this size means, Lorenzini invites us to consider the climatic history of the Earth. Palaeoclimatic studies based on air trapped for thousands of years deep in the ice of Antarctica and Greenland show that the mean temperature of the Earth increased about 10°C in the 4000-year period from the end of the last ice age, which occurred 14,000 years ago. The largest change in the mean temperature of the Earth, measured over a period of the order of a century, since the last ice age, was therefore about 0.25°C per century. The change predicted for the coming century, due to the increase in the greenhouse effect precipitated by man, is therefore ten times greater than historical values.

Living species adapted to the slow increase in temperature but it is reasonable to suppose that a ten-fold rate of change will be more devastating than changes that have hitherto occurred. Lorenzini explains that prediction of the effects of increased global warming in a complex system such as the Earth can only be carried out along very general lines with a variable probability level. According to a recent report of the Forum on Global Change Modelling, the most probable climatic and geophysical effects of atmospheric warming include a decrease in marine ice in the northern hemisphere, an increase in mean sea level of about 0.5 m before 2100 with flooding of lowlands of the Earth, retraction of river deltas, the disappearance of many beaches and a mean increase in rainfall due to increased mean levels of evaporation. The geographic distribution of rainfall is expected to change, with a probable decrease in internal continental areas and expansion of deserts, while storms will tend to replace winter snowfall in temperate regions. Local climatic changes are impossible to predict at the current state of the art. Changes associated with a lower probability include increased summer drought at middle latitudes of the northern hemisphere, increased climatic instability with amplification of extremes, and a higher frequency of hurricanes in the tropics.

Paradoxically, Lorenzini adds, some 'good' effects can also be expected. As far as the biosphere is concerned, agriculture is likely to adapt better to new climatic conditions than natural vegetation. New agricultural species suited to new climatic conditions will be introduced by man while many forests will die, unable to adapt or migrate sufficiently quickly to more congenial areas. Certain forest impact models estimate that a third of the world's forests will be modified by rapid global climatic change. Increased fire risk will presumably be associated with more intense drought in certain areas; increased flooding will be associated with increased rainfall in other areas, hand in hand with an increase in parasites due to warmer winters.

Lorenzini's research in collaboration with NASA involves the use of satellites to monitor the greenhouse effect. Referring to a paper published in *Nature*,[10] he goes on to mention a last, highly probable, point, namely that warming of the troposphere (from altitude 0 to 10 km) will be associated with cooling of the higher layers of the atmosphere, the stratosphere, mesosphere and thermosphere. An increase in the surface temperature of the Earth of 2.5°C is estimated to be accompanied by a drop in temperature of the thermosphere (above 80 km) by as much as 50°C. The lower thermosphere (between 80 and 150 km) therefore lends itself to the early detection of tropospheric warming by satellite. However, conventional satellites cannot orbit below 150 km because of high aerodynamic resistance. The recent use of tethered satellites makes it possible to reach altitudes of 110 km and, for brief periods, even lower altitudes. A satellite attached to a long cable let out by the space shuttle could orbit in the lower thermosphere and make the measurements necessary to determine thermospheric cooling, which is an amplified manifestation of global warming due to the increased greenhouse effect. These measurements would be an early warning signal of global climatic changes. Several US universities, including the Harvard-Smithsonian Institute, and several Italian universities (Rome, Siena, L'Aquila) have expressed interest in the use of this new spatial technology for studying future trends in climate. Lorenzini expressed the hope of successful collaboration between NASA and the Italian space agency in view of the social importance of environmental changes.

Refined and complex mathematical models have been used to describe scenarios of the increased greenhouse effect for different latitudes, predicted fuel consumptions and types of fuel. The different predictions are not incompatible with the experimental data already recorded or with the following conclusions:

a) The quantity of carbon dioxide in the atmosphere has clearly increased in the last 30 years.

---

[10] R.J. Cicerone, Greenhouse cooling up high, *Nature*, **8**, 344, 1990, 104-105.

b) Combustion of fossil fuels and conversion of forests into farmland involve a transfer of carbon to the atmosphere.

c) The increase in carbon dioxide can modify global climate, the biological systems upon which life depends and agriculture, with heavy repercussions on the global economy.

A period of natural cooling was forecast for the coming years, but the increased greenhouse effect is causing a super interglacial period, with the possibility of reaching the highest temperatures of the last thousand years in the coming century. As Lorenzini underlined, this means melting of polar ice, a rise in sea level and flooding of coastal cities and agricultural plains: gondolas in New York and the opening of the mythical north-west passage! The carbon dioxide will also lead to an increase in water vapour which will in turn contribute to the increased greenhouse effect. The overall result will be a further increase in temperature and disappearance of the intermediate seasons: severe summer droughts and conversion of semi-arid areas, including southern Europe, into deserts. This trend is already detectable in southern Italy and Spain.

The areas worst affected will be those near deserts and Third World countries with precarious agriculture. In 1983, drought hit Ghana and the Ivory Coast, aggravated by hot dusty winds from the desert. The desertification of Africa associated with carbon dioxide build-up has already begun. If the process continues, arable land will shift towards the poles, the south of the northern hemisphere, tropical countries and the Third World paying for the industrial activities and the insane energy consumption of industrialized countries. We run the risk of making our planet a desert hothouse and of mortgaging food production for the growing world population.

Most plants and animals would require millions of years to adapt to such large changes in the Earth's temperature. These changes can therefore be expected to lead to the extinction of many species of plants and animals; historical time and biological time are quite different scales.

On the other hand, if human society wants to guarantee a future for its descendants and life on this unique planet, it ought to adopt the conclusion of the US National Academy of Science, that the primary limiting factor of energy production from fossil fuels could be the climatic effects of carbon dioxide release.[11] This means making a change

---

[11] National Academy of Science, *Carbon dioxide and climate: a second assessment*, National Academy Press, Washington, 1982.

from fossil fuels to clean, renewable energy sources and limiting the growth of energy consumption. Only in this way can our particular biosphere continue its coevolutionary history!

A return to Ptolemy

Prigogine gives a clear and simple description of the ecodynamic peculiarities of the biosphere, which is far from being in a state of equilibrium because it is characterized by instability, bifurcations and dissipative chaos;[12] time is therefore real and plays a fundamental constructive role. If we assume that time is real, we have to reformulate dynamics, which includes irreversibility; this question will be dealt with in Chapter 8.

Thermodynamics and biological evolution introduce the concept of the unidirectional flow of time and shift our 'gestalt',[13] focussing attention on the relations between and evolution of structures rather than on single species and molecules. All natural processes are irreversible, maintained by a flow of negative entropy. Time, like entropy, is a natural trend. Time is stored in relations, and events have created biodiversity. The value of biodiversity and the concept of negative entropy are milestones for the new discipline of ecological economics and for a new physics concerned with ecology and systemic biology.

In my opinion, we apply a 'gestalt' of space to the concept of time. Space is reversible and isotropic; time is irreversible and anisotropic. In our thinking, time is an interval. For space we are accustomed to say: 'sixty kilometres from Florence to Siena or sixty kilometres from Siena to Florence.' We do the same with time: twenty years ago or twenty years until the year 2022; whereas time should be thought of as irreversible and expressed in terms of negative entropy, stored information, biodiversity, number of correlations, events, interactions.

[12] I. Prigogine, in: C. Rossi and E. Tiezzi (eds) *Ecological physical chemistry*, Elsevier, Amsterdam, 1991, pp. 1-24.

[13] In his famous monograph, *The structure of scientific revolution* (1962), Thomas Kuhn defines 'paradigms' as all those examples of scientific practice which provide models that give rise to traditions of coherent scientific research (Chap. II). Taking several intuitions from Butterfield (1949) *The origins of modern science*, and Hanson (1958) *The models of scientific discovery*, he compares changes of paradigm with changes in visual gestalt (lines on paper that were first seen as a bird are now seen as an antelope) which give the elements of a problem in a new perspective which enables a solution to be found for the first time. In this way, a change in paradigm is similar to a reorientation in gestalt (Chaps. VIII and X).

In a spatial concept of nature, the planet Earth is a small entity in a Cartesian diagram with spatial coordinates, in line with a correct Copernican view. In a temporal concept of nature, the planet Earth is a large entity in a hypothetical Cartesian diagram with temporal coordinates, in line with a challenging neo-Ptolemaic view.

In Milton's *Paradise lost*,[14] Adam asks the angel Raphael for an explanation of celestial motion. He receives a doubtful reply and is exhorted to concern himself with things more worthy to be known than the 'true' structure of the cosmos (the true 'system of the World' as it was called in the day of Copernicus, Kepler, Galileo and Newton). The angel Raphael asks whether it is indeed plausible that the Sun revolves around the mere 'spot' or 'graine' of the Earth every day:

...while the sedentarie Earth, ...
Serv'd by more noble then her self, attaines
Her end without least motion, and receaves,
As Tribute... her warmth and light?

Then the angel continues:

"Yet not to Earth are those bright Luminaries Officious, but to the Earths habitant", suggesting that there is reason to regard our cosmic homeland as privileged! But it is unlikely that Milton rejected Copernican ideas and clung to those of Aristotle and Ptolemy, since he openly admired Galileo, the 'Tuscan artist' who, with his telescope, radically changed our concept of the 'Fabric of the Heav'ns'. The answer is less obvious: from one point of view, transcending any type of anthropocentrism (as we should call it today), it is perfectly coherent to maintain the significance of the Earth for man while sustaining the Copernican viewpoint, hypothesizing not only terrestrial motion but even the plurality of worlds. Thus, the angel Raphael addresses Adam:

... What if the Sun
Be Center to the World, and other Starrs
By his attractive vertue and thir own
Incited, dance about him various rounds?
Their wandring course now high, now low, then hid,
Progressive, retrograde or standing still,
In six thou seest, and what if sev'nth to these
The Planet Earth, so stedfast though she seem,
Insensibly three different Motions move?

---

[14] J. Milton, *Paradise lost*, Book VIII, lines 1-38, 66-152.

Which else to several Sphears thou must ascribe,
Mov'd contrarie with thwart obliquities,
Or save the Sun his labour, and that swift
Nocturnal and Diurnal rhomb suppos'd,
Invisible else above all Starrs, the Wheele
Of Day and Night; which needs not thy beleefe,
If Earth industrious of her self fetch Day
Travelling East, and with her part averse
From the Suns beam meet Night, her other part
Still luminous by his ray. What if that light
Sent from her through the wide transpicuous aire,
To the terrestrial Moon be as a Starr
Enlightening her by Day, as she by Night
This Earth? reciprocal, if Land be there,
Fields and Inhabitants: Her spots thou seest
As Clouds, and Clouds may rain, and Rain produce
Fruits in her soft'nd Soile, for some to eate
Allotted there; and other Suns perhaps
With thir attendant Moons thou wilt descrie
Communicating Male and Female Light,
Which two great Sexes animate the World,
Stor'd in each Orb perhaps with some that live."

Today we find ourselves in a double perspective not so different from that sketched in the dialogue between Raphael and Adam. For Milton, the controversy between followers of Copernicus and Ptolemy was a recent intellectual event, and continued while he was writing *Paradise Lost*. A double cosmology seemed at least to be a way of halting discussion and emphasizing the gap between the conjectures of our limited, fallible minds and the unfathomable divine plan. For us, the task is to realise our responsibility as citizens of the Earth. It is obviously not necessary to question the spatial coordinates of the Earth, its position in the solar system, its smallness in the universe, its roundness. Our task is simply to give time the scientific dignity it deserves.

8

HIC SUNT LEONES

Collisions between molecules

In the beginning, a great void, infinite spaces. Two molecules meet, recognize each other, exchange energy in collision and proceed on different paths. Their meeting causes changes in energy and direction. The new directions embody the information of the event: a collision occurred and the information it left cannot be cancelled. The new direction carries the memory of the collision.

Along the new path the first molecule meets another. Later in the 'time of events' there are other collisions and relations, between three, four and more molecules, relations of a higher order, according to the natural order ticked out by the 'time of events'. Nobel Prize winner Ilya Prigogine[1] speaks of 'natural time ordering'. Relations between molecules occur as a consequence of previous events: the evolution of events influences subsequent events in a stochastic way.

Our molecule goes on its way, carrying the memory and information of the events in which it has participated. It meets other molecules and 'chooses' to react with some, forming new, generally more complex molecules. In the primeval broth of simple molecules such as carbon dioxide and urea, larger and more complex molecules form. These take different conformations in space with different internal energy distributions. During its history, therefore, the molecule takes different forms; the history of events is transformed into structure, form, aesthetic content, on the basis of chance and the choices made by the initial molecules. Chance and choice mean stochastic process; biological evolution is stochastic; the flow of events and forms is stochastic; our learning process is stochastic because even our minds are part of that

---

[1] I. Prigogine, in C. Rossi and E. Tiezzi (eds), *Ecological physical chemistry*, Elsevier, Amsterdam, 1991, pp. 1-24.

marvellous history of coevolution which is the history of life and the biosphere.

Now our molecule is bonded to many others in the double helix of DNA, the nucleic acid that is the basis of genetics and the transmission of information and heredity. Aesthetic characteristics, such as eye colour and the patterns of plumage and butterfly wings, are also trasmitted in this way. The 'time of events' is now embodied in the information transmitted by DNA, in the complexity of DNA itself, products of an evolutionary history in which collisions, relations, and changes of direction and energy abounded. The 'time of events' is transformed into the 'time of things' and is an intrinsic property of molecular information and the structure of matter.

The time paradox

The equations of classical physics have no notion of the 'time of events' or the 'time of things'. Prigogine and Stengers[2] write that although quantum mechanics and general relativity are revolutionary, as far as the concept of time is concerned they are direct descendants of classical dynamics and carry a radical negation of the irreversibility of time.

The recognition that time is 'real' leads to what Prigogine calls the 'time paradox'. He asks how it is possible that the basic equations of classical and quantum mechanics are reversible with respect to time at the microscopic level whereas at the macroscopic level the arrow of time plays a fundamental role. How can time emerge from non-time?

To solve this paradox, Prigogine starts with Poincaré's theorem of 1889, introducing the distinction between integrable and non-integrable systems. The latter lead to an alternative formulation of dynamics in probabilistic terms, both in classical and quantum physics. This descripton includes the breaking of time symmetry and incorporates the Second Law of Thermodynamics. The new theory on which the Brussels school is working may have important practical applications in ecology. Classical and quantum physics have practically nothing to contribute to the study of complex ecological systems in a process of evolution.

Prigogine considers Large Poincaré Systems including multiple-body systems involving collisions. He treats them in a way that implies the existence of chaos in the context of dynamics, always regarded as the

---

[2] I. Prigogine and I. Stengers, *Entre le temps et l'eternité*, Fayard, Paris, 1988.

stronghold of a deterministic description. Broken time symmetry and irreversibility erupt in the core of dynamics. Prigogine[1] writes of the inversion of the usual formulation of the time paradox. The usual attempt was to deduce the arrow of time from dynamics based on reversible time equations. He speaks of generalizing dynamics to include irreversibility. The divergences of Poincaré are eliminated by an appropriate time ordering of the dynamic states.

In this way Prigogine introduces the concept of the natural time ordering of dynamic states. To understand what this means, let us take the example of a stone that falls into a pond and causes ripples. We may also have the inverse situation in which incoming waves eject a stone. It is true that only the first event ever occurs. Natural time ordering has the falling stone first and then the ripples. In order to give meaning to the Poincaré denominators, the time of dynamic states must also be ordered: first the unstable atomic state, and then the emission of radiation. Prigogine goes on to say that natural time ordering must also be introduced into statistical descriptions. This integrates Large Poincaré Systems into quite general situations and creates a new dynamics which breaks radically with the past.

In a classical gas, the particles collide and these collisions give rise to relations. At first we have binary relations, and then ternary relations until more and more particles are involved. Prigogine considers the example of two persons in conversation; this can be regarded as a collision. When the persons leave each other, the memory of their conversation remains. The unidirectionality of relationships breaks the symmetry of the classical description; the time of relationships evolves. Transitions involving higher-order relations are 'future-oriented'; those involving lower-order relations are 'past-oriented'. In the old situation, there was microscopic reversibility and macroscopic irreversibility of time. Now we have a new microscopic level with broken time symmetry from which a dissipative macroscopic level emerges.

Prigogine concludes that irreversibility is not related to Newtonian time or its Einsteinian generalization, but to an 'internal time' expressed in terms of the relations between the various units of which the system is composed, as are relations between particles. We cannot stop the flow of relations or the decay of unstable atomic states. These concepts bring us to the threshold of a new physics incorporating dynamics, instability, chaos and irreversibility: an evolutionary physics based on the assumptions of Prigogine.

On Roman maps, the unexplored areas of Africa were labeled *hic sunt leones*. So as not to admit the problems of exploration and the limits of conquest, or more simply because they were not areas of economic interest, the geographers of the time avoided the problem by stating merely that there were lions.

Time has had a similar fate in science. The science of Descartes, Newton and Einstein, having failed to harness time in rational models, solved the problem by eliminating it. Time is only an illusion of the mind, according to Einstein; contrary to all evidence, time is measured reversibly like space in Newtonian and quantum mechanics; time that passes has no place in classical science, where two dogmas negate the flow of time.

One is the dogma of reversibility and the other is the dogma of the reproducible experiment. In all Western schools and universities it is taught that an experiment has scientific value only if it is reproducible, only if the same result can be obtained again later. This may be true for a machine or an inanimate object that changes only in the timescale of geological eras, but it is certainly not true for biological or ecological experiments. A living creature or an ecosystem obeys the laws of biological evolution; at any time it is different from what it was an instant before. This is the essence of life. In biology and ecology, reproducible experiments do not exist, and for science, time does not exist: *hic sunt leones*.

We can conclude that biological evolution and ecology are not sciences or, more wisely, with Prigogine,[2] that the fact that quantum mechanics cannot tell us the probability that a quantum transition will occur in a given moment, means that for us this formalism is incomplete. If we intend taking the notion of time, life and the associated Uncertainty Principle seriously, we have to modify the notion of the observable in quantum mechanics and give an intrinsic meaning, independent of the act of observation, to the probabilistic dispersal of energy. In other words, we have to accentuate the probabilistic character of the theory and not the deterministic or subjective character. Time is in matter; it is in the nature of the molecules; it is an integral part of biological evolution. Either we modify our reversible deterministic paradigms, or we do what Palomar did, forcing reality into the straitjacket of atemporality.

Prigogine and Stengers add that the theories of relativity, cosmology and quantum mechanics have always sought separation from the time dimension, placing the laws of time in the dimension of eternity. However, our life is not governed by atemporal and deterministic laws, but is immersed in the flow of time, in constant relation with memory of the past and projection towards the future.

Boltzmann denied irreversibility, regarding it as a defeat; the physicists of Einstein's generation made this negation a scientific dogma. As Poincaré pointed out in 1889,[3] nothing more sophisticated than plain logic is needed to reveal the error of trying to explain irreversibility in terms of the reversible.

---

[3] H.Poincaré, Sur les tentatives d'explication mécanique des principes de la thermodynamique, *Comptes rendus de l'Académie des Sciences*, **CVIII**, 1889, 550-553.

9

EVOLUTIONARY CONSERVATION
OR CONSERVATIVE EVOLUTION?

The discussion between Bohr and Einstein at the Solvay Conference

The fifth Solvay Conference, 'Electrons and Protons' (1927), went down in history because of the discussion between Niels Bohr and Albert Einstein. At the time, Bohr was right; however, at the twelfth Solvay Conference 'Quantum Theory of Fields' (1961), Bohr commented that at the conference thirty years earlier, he had been invited to speak on the epistemological problems of quantum physics, especially the question of appropriate terminology and complementarity. The main argument was that the unambiguous communication of physical evidence requires that the experimental method and the recording of observations be expressed in a common language, appropriately refined from the vocabulary of classical physics.

But what does 'the vocabulary of classical physics' mean? And what is the relation between experiment and theory? Is it possible to imagine a reproducible experiment in biology or ecology? Biological evolution and time irreversibility suggest not.

Let us return to Niels Bohr and the comments of Prigogine at the twentieth Solvay Conference, 'Quantum Optics' (1992), on the occasion of the eightieth anniversary of the first Solvay Conference, 'Radiation Theory and Quanta' (1912). Prigogine commented that in Bohr's view, the measuring device had to be an intermediary between the laws of quantum mechanics, valid at a microscopic level, and the world of classical physics. Before quantum physics, this problem did not exist because it was assumed that the dynamics of atoms was the same as that of large bodies. In quantum theory, the situation is completely different. Prigogine observed that Schrödinger's equation was time reversible and could not lead to irreversible processes. He went on to say that this dilemma could now be solved and Bohr's intuitions confirmed (see Appendix). In order to communicate with nature, he said, a common time was needed; the results of measurements had to be read in 'our' time, not in that associated with Schrödinger's equation.

Prigogine gives a mathematical treatment of this problem based on Poincaré's theorem in his *Dissipative processes in quantum theory*.[1] Obviously this goes beyond the scope of our discussion (some points are amplified in the Appendix). However, one thing which emerged was that it is now possible to talk of 'quantum chaos'; Prigogine's treatment defines the limits of orthodox quantum theory, leads to solutions with broken time symmetry, enables irreversibility to be introduced at microscopic level and introduces 'lifetimes' associated with dissipative processes. The traditional perspective, present in classical and quantum physics, that stable systems are the rule and unstable systems an exception is now inverted. Dissipation becomes a basic part of microscopic systems.

Prigogine concludes that measurement is a way of communicating with nature, but requires a common concept of time which emerges from dissipation. Hence, our possibility of communicating with the quantum world depends on instability as a consequence of quantum chaos (the measuring apparatus and the system are described in the same way). Schrödinger's cat[2] is a living creature and life cannot be divorced from irreversible processes.

Prigogine maintains that Bohr was right in the famous discussion with Einstein, but when quantum theory was formulated, dynamic instability and chaos were not in the perspectives of normal physics. These concepts are now essential for the self-consistency of quantum physics. The subjective aspects of quantum mechanics have been eliminated.

---

[1] I. Prigogine, Dissipative processes in quantum theory, *Physics report*, **219**, 1992, 93-108.

[2] Schrödinger imagined the situation of a cat in a steel box with the following infernal device (out of reach of the cat): a Geiger counter with a small quantity of radioactive material in its tube, such a small quantity that although one of its atoms could decay within an hour, it is just as probable that it will not. If the atom decays, the tube of the counter becomes incandescent and activates a hammer which breaks a phial of prussic acid. If the system remains isolated for an hour, we can say that the cat will stay alive provided that no atom decays in that time. The first atom to break down would kill the cat. The function psi for the whole system gives an expression in which the live cat and the dead cat are present to the same extent. E. Schrödinger, Dei gegenwarige Situation in der Quanten-mechanik, *Naturwessenschaften*, **23**, 1935, 807-812, 844-849. For a critical comment see A. Whitaker, *Einstein, Bohr and the quantum dilemma*, Cambridge University Press, Cambridge 1996, Chap.6.

Poincaré's divergence (see Appendix) is a mathematical fact independent of the observer. This leads to a new formulation of quantum theory and forces us to accept a view of nature which includes instability and dissipation.

In this work of Prigogine, the foundations of evolutionary physics are laid. The scientific schizophrenia that separated evolutionary biology and mechanics has been overcome and physics and biology find a meeting point. We now have glimpses of the potential of new instruments of physical chemistry for tackling the complexity of living systems and evolving ecosystems. The myth of the reproducible experiment no longer binds us. Ecodynamic models (see Ch. 7) begin to give the first results in complex fields such as sustainable towns, integrated agro-energy systems, biomass and aquatic ecosystems. Physical chemistry comes down from its pedestal of pure theory, abandoning unreal molecular monads for the real world; it leaves its ivory tower of useless purity and comes to grips with nature, society, the bios and the oikos, the complexity of the true problems of humanity and our planet, without compromising its rigour and scientific character.

Entropy and the leaf

Thermodynamics and entropy are the tools necessary for opening the doors of evolution in environmental modelling. Entropy changes over time in living systems are one of the basic problems of biological thermodynamics. A living system tends to a state of minimum entropy; in other words, the entropy of an organism decreases, reaches a minimum and remains at that level. However, if we study a system far from equilibrium and just slightly complex, such as the leaf of a deciduous plant, things become more complicated. Ichiro Aoki demonstrated that the entropy of a leaf varies over the period of a day and is proportional to the solar energy absorbed.[3]

The entropy patterns of living systems are still in need of much research. The 'principle of maximum power' of Lotka and Odum is in line with an increase in entropy, whereas the 'principle of minimum entropy' of Nicolis and Prigogine seems to contradict it. Actually, in the second case we are dealing with systems close to equilibrium, whereas ecosystems are typical

---

[3] I. Aoki, Entropy budgets of deciduous plant leaves and a theorem of oscillating entropy production, *Bulletin of mathematical biology*, **49**, 1987, 449-460.

far-from-equilibrium systems and the special thermodynamics of Prigogine is required for such systems.[4] Although few complex ecosystems have yet been studied in detail using this approach, it is likely, as Aoki suggests, that entropy varies with time during development, remains constant in an intermediate (steady) phase and varies again in the senescent phase. In the study of biophysical systems, much attention was dedicated in the past to energy flows, and the same approach was used for interactions with the environment (for example, the ecological studies of Odum and Odum[5]). In thermodynamics, however, the energy viewpoint does not tell us half the story.

The first principle of thermodynamics is concerned with energy, whereas the second is concerned with entropy. As Landsberg observed,[6] the first states that internal energy exists and the second that entropy exists. This is a big step because it overcomes the old dilemma of whether entropy was the shadow of energy or vice versa, and does not reduce the ingenious invention of entropy to a purely energy dogma. The first principle formulates the concept of energy in a conservation framework; the second formulates that of entropy in an evolutionary framework. This is where evolutionary biology and mechanics meet. Schrödinger's introduction of the concept of negentropy was an inspired one: a living system absorbs negentropy from the external environment, structuring itself and evolving on the basis of this interaction. In other words, energy and entropy can be related, as is done in classical thermodynamics and statistical thermodynamics, but from the point of view of time, the two concepts are irreducible and different. In an evolutionary gestalt, entropy has an extra gear which is the key necessary for studying living systems and ecology. It is important to study flows of energy and matter, quantities which are intrinsically conserved; it is also important to study entropy flows, an intrinsically evolutionary and non-conserved quantity. The appearance of a term of entropy production, or 'source term' as Aoki[7] calls it, is the watershed dividing the evolutionary world from the special case of conserved energy and mass. But if energy and mass are intrinsically conserved and entropy is intrinsically

    [4] See Chapter 6.

    [5] H.T. Odum, *Systems ecology - an introduction*, John Wiley, New York, 1983, H.T Odum & E.C. Odum, *Energy basis for man and nature*, McGraw Hill, New York, 1981.

    [6] P. Landsberg, The Fourth Law of Thermodynamics, *Nature*, **238**, 1972, 229-231.

    [7] I. Aoki, Entropy laws in ecological networks at steady state, *Ecological modelling*, **42**, 1988, 289-303.

evolutionary, how can entropy be calculated on the basis of energy and mass quantities?[8] This question is still unanswered[9] and all we can do is to note that the ecodynamic viewpoint is different from that of classical physics and classical ecology, as indicated in Table 1.

**Table 1. Comparison of ecodynamics,
classical physics and ecology**

	Classical physics	Ecology	Ecodynamics
Basic world view	mechanistic dynamic molecular	evolutionary molecular	evolutionary systemic
Time	reversible	evolutionary	irreversible evolutionary
Focus	object subject quantity nature	object subject quality quantity nature	relations between quantity-quality and between subject-object
Viewpoint	reductionist	reductionist holistic	holistic
Goal	knowledge	survival of species	sustainable development
Modelling	deterministic	evolutionary	evolutionary systemic irreversible

---

[8] It is impossible to calculate the entropy of living systems. The trick up to now has been to assume that a system is composed of elements, and to apply classical thermodynamics to each of them.

[9] See for example the interesting considerations of P. Coveney, Chaos, entropy and the arrow of time, in *Chaos - a science for the real world*, N. Hall (ed), Italian translation F. Muzzio, Padua, 1992, pp. 203-212.

10

THE ANTI-AESTHETIC ASSUMPTION
OF NEWTON AND DESCARTES

See the colours

Observation of nature teaches us that quality and time are external parameters but inherent properties of living things. Quality and time play fundamental roles in biological evolution, contributing to the evolutionary success of species and modelling forms of life. In a systemic ecological framework, these two categories, basic assumptions of the epistemology of evolution, can today be regarded as true values to be taken into account in scientific education and programming sustainable development.

In science, we need to call into question the anti-aesthetic assumption, criticised by Gregory Bateson, on which Newtonian physics and Cartesian philosophy are based. According to this assumption, we can deal only with measurable quantities.

In living systems, the determinant role of time in transforming molecular and biological structures, and of form in the relations between species, is evident. The value 'quality' is thus recovered and the scientific importance of the aesthetics of nature underlined. In a new non-linear and systemic framework, plots and narrative add clarity and complexity to the scientific discourse. Red, orange, yellow, green, blue, indigo and violet, the seven colours of the solar spectrum, have been woven in an infinity of relationships by biological evolution: colours in time, colours as structure and form, colours as exchange of information between us and the environment.

Molecules, electrons and nuclei are in continuous movement, jumping from one energy level to another, folding, twisting, stretching, vibrating, rotating and spinning. These movements generate electromagnetic radiation, with its dual (wave-particle) nature. The electromagnetic spectrum ranges from high-energy X-rays and gamma-rays, to low-energy microwaves and radio waves, and the colours of the visible band are more or less in the middle. Red is at the low-energy (low frequency) and violet at the high-energy (high frequency) end of the visible spectrum, corresponding to longer and shorter wavelengths respectively. Beyond the red, there is the invisible, lower frequency infrared, which causes the increased greenhouse effect because it is trapped by atmospheric carbon dioxide. Beyond the violet is the higher-frequency ultraviolet which causes tanning of the skin, but if it is not filtered by the ozone layer, it can cause skin tumours and arrest photosynthesis and plant growth. Together, the seven colours of the rainbow give white light as we know it; when they are absent, there is darkness, blackness.

The colours should be seen in their overall complexity, as electromagnetic radiation and emotions and sensations at the same time, if we are to appreciate fully the relations between the mind of man and the nature of matter and energy. 'Objective' science has reduced colours to a frequency and blue to pure 440 nanometre radiation. 'Subjective' art submits the existence of colour to the subject and has reduced colour to pure sensation.

If we want to see orange as a blue orange also, without foregoing the orange, or if we want to cross-fertilize science with art and art with science, we need to talk about relations, connecting structures, interactions between the subject and the object observed. In other words, the colour green of a plant exists independently of the fact that we see it, for the very reason that it existed millions of years before the human mind. Before man appeared on the earth, it was recognized by millions of plant and animal organisms. But it is also true that in observing a plant, our mind begins a series of interpretations, of rational and intuitive syntheses, and weaves a series of relations with the plant and with the emotions evoked by the plant, coloured by our culture and genetic heritage.

This means uniting microscopic and macroscopic, going beyond the dichotomy of reductionism and antireductionism, studying biological phenomena in terms of relations and self-organization, in order to see the global coherence of the single parts. It means adopting a philosophy of nature that I would define as Lucretian, in which aesthetics is determinant in the study of science, economics and politics, and in weaving the first new alphabet of a discourse between ourselves and nature. It means recognizing the need, as Bateson did,[1] to abolish the anti-aesthetic assumption that all phenomena can and must be studied in quantitative terms. This assumption arose from the importance that Bacon, Locke and Newton attributed to the physical sciences. It means recognizing that quality and form have scientific value.

Time, understood as the number of relations in, and as information stored in, the energy-matter system, models the molecular forms of biological evolution. Time is not an abstraction, it is an integral part of matter; it is part of what exists; no political, social or economic theory is possible which does not take the irreversibility of time into account. The problem of time is fundamental because the structures that connect us with others, and which are an integral part of the co-evolution of nature and the human mind, have time embodied in them. Without time we cannot explain how these structures change and how they proceed. It is not a question of giving up rational thought but rather of recovering a series of ethical and aesthetic values, of going all the way into what Gregory Bateson calls ecology of the mind and of asking ourselves about the structures that connect the sequoia to the crab, the crab to the sea anemone, the sea anemone to the amoeba, the amoeba to the schizophrenic and all this to us. In other words, it means asking ourselves about the structure connecting man with nature in the enormously complex history of biological evolution, and reconstructing the values and ways of thinking that will lead to such integration, bearing in mind that we are simultaneously 100% nature and 100% culture. Only from an awareness of this kind can the foundations emerge that will allow us to take up the challenge of complexity.

Environments, niches and species co-evolved and are co-evolving at different rates and times in the framework of great laws of nature which predate the mind and ideologies of man. Nature is never stationary; as it changes it sends a continuous flux of information to the mind of man, and man, by choosing, interacts with and broadly modifies nature: two entities, man and nature, are continuously exchanging information.

The nymph Echo, Golem-robot, Gargantua and Pantagruel

The universe consists of relations between matter and energy. Music, sounds, words are energies that weave relations between different

[1] G. Bateson, *Steps to an ecology of mind*, Chandler Publishing Company, New York, 1972.

biological species. In this splendid interplay, the aesthetic component is essential. To reduce sound waves to mathematical models and quantitative measures is to lose much biological meaning. Aesthetics could be the key to superseding a purely quantitative scientific view and to introducing the basic ecological category of quality. Quality of life requires aesthetics. Aesthetic values must be the basis of a much-needed turning point of civilization.

The jaguar, heart-of-the-mountain, is the lord of the echo and of drums in Maya culture. Among the Yurucare, the Bakairi of Xingù, the Caribs, and the Warai of Guyana it is said that to escape decimation by the human hero, the last of the jaguars was taken in and hidden by the Moon. Since then he has lived with her and moves only by night. In the same way the nymph Echo of Greek mythology is identified with the forests and mountains, and was turned to stone, the form of which models sound.

In quite a different way, that I would term anthropocentric and anti-aesthetic, Echo is coupled with the Hebrew Golem: Golem-Echo as the idea of something double. Unlike Gustav Meyrink,[2] I have always seen Golem, the red-clay giant built by man, as a creature of the sorcerer's apprentice, a robot-man (among other things, Golem is generally dumb whereas the nymph Echo speaks in dulcet tones), the stupid slave and destroyer. He is a symbol of the unnatural machine, the cathedral of red clay in the desert, the nuclear mega power station, big and stupid. Like all the things made by sorcerers' apprentices, Golem escapes from the scientist's control, and grows gigantic. He incarnates the myth of growth which in ecology has the opposite characteristic to development. Growth is cancer, pure quantity without quality, the negation of balance and wisdom.

When the sorcerer writes the Hebrew word for death on Golem's forehead, Golem collapses and turns back into formless clay. Often, however, in mythology, he crushes the sorcerer as he falls. The sorcerer becomes the victim of his own machine. For the technocrat who has lost his aesthetic sense (together with his ecological conscience), we can say, as Mephistopheles did, that our first action is free but we are slaves for the second, or free to enter but servants in leaving.

The two wonderful giants of Rabelais, Gargantua and Pantagruel, are of a different nature. Wandering clergyman, rich in deuteroculture, first

---

[2] G. Meyrink, *Il Golem*, Italian translation, Bompiani, Milan, 1987.

monk and then surgeon and writer, Rabelais created these two complex characters and, with the birds and arabesqued cages of Ringing Island, a beautiful image of sound. Pantagruel embarks with his companions for the Sea of Chaos, but unlike Ulysses in Dante, he saves himself and his crew by landing on the Island of Macroaeons where the people live long lives and know how to find a balance between technical capacity and respect for the environment.[3]

---

[3] F. Rabelais, *Gargantua and Pantagruel*, Books V and VI.

11

TOWARDS AN EVOLUTIONARY PHYSICS

Il sogno è l'infinita ombra del Vero
(Dreams are the infinite shadow of Truth)
Giovanni Pascoli

Unsustainable dualism

Western science conceives of nature in terms of geometric rules and mechanistic laws. Newton's laws, for example, are reversible deterministic laws that imply certainty and assume that time is symmetrical between past and future. Prigogine[1] adds and counterposes the concept of 'events' to 'laws of nature' of this kind. We know that such laws are not true for living systems, ecosystems, or the events of biology and ecology.

Quantum theory and relativity, the two great revolutions in physics of the last century, incorporate the determinism and reversibility of Newton's laws unchanged; uncertainty, irreversibility and the role of time are not accorded scientific dignity. This leads to a schizophrenic dualism between being and evolving, between the static description of nature and the irreversible behaviour of living things.

Prigogine[2] finds this dualism in Steven Hawking's *A brief history of time:*[3] on the one hand, the static universe, and on the other, humans, who evolved and for whom other laws and principles are applicable. In fact Hawking introduces what he terms an anthropic principle and identifies the thermodynamic arrow of time with the psychological arrow of time (namely the fact that our minds distinguish past and future). However, humans are not the only beings to have evolved; plants and animals were

---

[1] I. Prigogine, *Laws and events: the concept of nature*, OIKOS lecture, Siena, November, 1994.
[2] I. Prigogine, *The coming together of western and eastern points of view on science and nature*, MOA lecture, Japan, May, 1994.
[3] S. Hawking, *A brief history of time*, Bantam Books, New York, 1988.

here hundreds of millions of years before the human mind made its appearance on this planet.

It does not seem possible to reconcile classical physics and evolutionary biology. Darwin is left out on the doorstep as far as certain branches of Western science are concerned. On the one hand we have the deterministic reversible 'laws of nature', and on the other, the laws of thermodynamics and entropy ready to offer us the basis for a new evolutionary physics. The Greek word 'entropy' means evolution.

Today we know that chemical reactions and biological processes produce entropy or negentropy, distinguish between past and future, and are truly irreversible. We know that in systems far from equilibrium new structures are created, that order arises from disorder and that coherence can emerge. Prigogine underlines the existence of a time paradox: 'laws of nature' on the one hand which negate irreversibility; on the other, the fundamental time dimension without which it is impossible to conceive our existence. Neither biologically nor cosmologically can nature be described without distinguishing between past and future. We live in an ecosystem kept far from equilibrium by solar radiation. The non-equilibrium processes discussed in Chapter 6 and the consequent inclusion of time in non-linear equations are the basis of a *new evolutionary physics* described in terms of probabilities.

To go towards an evolutionary view of physics means going in the direction of the unification of science and the humanities. *Science has given too much space to space, ignoring time.* In history, in human affairs*, in ecology, the role of time is fundamental: memories are certainly more important than kilometres.*

The search for certainties has dominated the western world for centuries. Marcello Cini[4,5] stresses that the very language of Newtonian physics is based on a deterministic conception and on the certainty that all phenomena are completely predictable in terms of simple and universal laws of nature. The limits of determinism, however, do not lie only in presuming to extrapolate the laws of the pendulum to the whole world, but in the negation of the irreversibility of nature.

According to Prigogine,[2,6] there are only two choices: either everything was determined at the moment of the big bang (including this book) or the universe evolves and novelties appear during its evolution, in which case the laws of nature cannot be deterministic but have to be expressed

⁴ M. Cini, *Un paradiso perduto*, Feltrinelli, Milan, 1994.
⁵ M. Cini in E. Tiezzi (ed.), *Ecologia e* ...., Laterza, Bari, 1995.
⁶ I. Prigogine, personal communication.

in terms of probabilities. He recalls Einstein's claim that the irreversibility of time was an illusion. Prigogine attempts to explain Einstein's attachment to this idea on the basis that Einstein was living in a very difficult period and that science was a way of escaping the turmoil of everyday life. Prigogine asks whether this view is still valid today. Is today's science a way of escaping from towns, or should science tackle the problem of pollution and improve town life?

I believe the days of the scientist in his ivory tower and of flights into pure reason are over. Today is a time of complete reimmersion in life, nature, our history of co-evolution, the uncertain irreversible history of biological phenomena to which we belong, and the history of our planet, since "we are lucky to live in a universe which has allowed life, art and beauty".[2]

At a time when we are collectively gambling with the destiny of our species, the awakening of an awareness of earthly community is a key event which may enable us to emerge from a barbarian age. It may do so by making us conscious of the fact that our solidarity is with this planet and on this planet. It is our Earth-homeland.[7]

To be ecological means to live in harmony with nature, accepting its diversity (sameness is not in the nature of things) and its uncertainty; otherwise creativity, the essence of art and science, is denied. It means having to do with chaos, not in the sense of ignorance, but as a mathematical theory for tackling complex situations that have many solutions and which can only be described in terms of probabilities, as we shall see in the next section.

A boat on the river, or systems sensitive to initial conditions

Who of us has never watched from a bridge as a paper boat is carried by the current? In Joyce's *Ulysses*, events in the life of the protagonists parallel the fate of a paper boat on the Liffey. The boat is caught in an eddy, or meets an obstacle. The minimum change in the initial position and speed of the boat can radically modify its course. Small changes in time lead to larger changes; this is a characteristic of chaos.[8] One of the principal scholars of what is known as deterministic chaos claims that

---

[7] E. Morin and A.B. Kern, *Terre-patrie*, Editions du Seuil, Paris, 1993.

[8] I. Percival, Il caos: una scienza per il mondo reale, in N. Hall (ed.), *Caos*, F. Muzzio, Padova, pp. 1-11.

determinism and long-term unpredictability coexist in situations of this kind, but if a paper boat confounds our powers of prediction, what about the motion of planets, weather patterns and the fate of empires? These interesting questions have different answers. The motion of planets can be predicted for centuries, whereas weather forecasts do not go beyond a week or two. It is very ambitious to talk about the fate of empires and the history of man, but some conclusions are possible, and these conclusions favour unpredictability.[9]

These various examples are what mathematicians call dynamic systems. Some of these systems never depend on initial conditions, others are sensitive to any initial condition, others have a mixture of these two features; long-term prediction is possible for certain initial conditions, but not for others. These mixed situations are often the most interesting. Our ancestors discovered at an early stage that it was difficult to predict the future and that small events can have large effects. A more recent discovery has been that in certain systems, a small change in an initial condition habitually leads to so many such changes that long-term predictions become quite impossible. This was demonstrated by the French mathematician Jacques Hadamard towards the end of the nineteenth century. At the time, Hadamard was only about thirty; he lived to almost a hundred, dying in 1963.[9]

In his masterpiece *La théorie physique* (1906), Pierre Duhem grasps the philosophical portent of Hadamard's results.[10] If any physical situation could be described by a mathematical model in the framework of the dynamic systems studied by Hadamard, the 'mathematical deductions' obtained from the model would be of no physical interest because the small uncertainties always present in the initial conditions would lead to a large uncertainty in the calculated trajectory after a long enough time, which would make the prediction useless. In the same period another French scientist was writing books on the philosophy of science; he was the famous Henri Poincaré. In *Science et Méthode*, Poincaré discusses the

[9] D. Ruelle, *Caso e caos*, Italian translation, Bollati Boringhieri, Turin, 1992 and 1993, see Chap. VIII.

[10] J. Hadamard, "Les surfaces à courbures opposées et leurs lignes géodésiques", *Journal de mathématiques pures et appliquées,* **4**, 1898, 729-775. P. Duhum, *La teoria fisica*, Italian translation, Il Mulino, Bologna 1978, part II, Chap. III. For a biographic profile of the mathematician J. Hadamard, who held that choice was governed by a sense of beauty, at least in mathematics, see B. Sassoli, biographical note, in J. Hadamard, *La psicologia dell'invenzione in campo matematico*, Italian translation, Cortina, Milan, 1993.

problem of unpredictability in a non-technical manner. He does not cite Hadamard or the mathematical details of the theory of dynamic systems (a theory he knew better than anyone else, having written it himself). An essential observation of Poincaré was that chance and determinism are rendered compatible by long-term unpredictability. He expressed this concept by saying that when a very small event that escapes us causes a large effect that we cannot miss, we say that the effect was due to chance. Poincaré knew how useful probabilities are in examining the physical world. He knew that chance is part of everyday life, and because he also believed in classical determinism (in his day quantum indeterminism had not yet been formulated), he wanted to discover where chance originated. His reflections provided various answers. In other words, he saw different mechanisms by which the classical deterministic description of the world could naturally lead to probabilistic idealization. One of these mechanisms was sensitivity to initial conditions.[9]

One example he gave was of unstable equilibrium. We know that a cone standing on its point will fall, but we do not know to which side. It seems that chance decides the side to which the cone falls. If the cone is perfectly symmetrical and its axis perfectly vertical and if it is not under the influence of any force but gravity, it will not fall. The slightest flaw in symmetry or weight distribution will make it lean to one side or another, and if it leans, even slightly, it will fall to that side. Even if its symmetry is perfect, a breath of air could make it lean a second of an arc, enough to determine its fall and the direction of the fall, which will be the same direction as the initial inclination.

A second very similar example is meteorological. Why do meteorologists have so much trouble in accurately forecasting the weather? Why do rain and storms seem to arrive by chance, so that many people find it natural to pray for rain or fine weather, whereas they would consider it ridiculous to pray for an eclipse? We notice that large perturbations generally occur where the atmosphere is in unstable equilibrium. The meteorologists see that this equilibrium is unstable and that a cyclone will occur somewhere, but they cannot say exactly where; a tenth of a degree this way or that at any point, and the cyclone breaks out here and not there, devastating areas that it would otherwise have spared. Had we known this tenth of a degree, we would have known in advance, but observations were neither close nor precise enough, and so it all seems due to chance. We find the same contrast between a small event that the observer cannot detect, and effects that may be tremendous disasters.[11]

Poincaré's ideas on meteorology do not seem to have received recognition until the age of computers. Perhaps the mathematician was ahead of his time.[12] If his ideas had been known outside the world of specialist mathematicians, and appreciated by naturalists, they would have given mathematical substance to the claims of the pioneers of ecology.

De minimis non curat lex, and so?

The lesson of Poincaré is quite general for an understanding of ecological equilibria. In the words of Marsh:

> It is a legal maxim that 'the law concerneth not itself with trifles', *de minimis non curat lex*; but in the vocabulary of nature, little and great are terms of comparison only; she knows no trifles, and her laws are as inflexible in dealing with an atom as with a continent or planet. The human operations mentioned in the last few paragraphs, therefore, do act in the ways ascribed to them, though our limited faculties are at present, perhaps forever, incapable of weighing their immediate, still more their ultimate consequences.[13]

As Poincaré guessed, it is only permissible to ignore what seems to us small if we first know the initial condition of a system to a given approximation and the mathematical model allows us to predict a later condition to *the same approximation*. This does not always happen; sometimes small differences in the initial conditions generate enormous differences by the end. In such cases, prediction is impossible.[14] This does not mean renouncing science, but that science can no longer be understood in the positivist sense of an instrument of prediction and hence dominion over nature. Science must now be understood as a necessary instrument of attention towards the delicacy of our

---

[11] H. Poincaré, Scienza e metodo, Italian translation, in *Opere epistemologiche*, G. Boniolo (ed.), vol.II, Piovan, Abano Terme 1989, pp.5-197.

[12] See Ruelle, footnote 9, who observed that in Poincaré's day, there were no fast calculators and the scientific community did not yet have the basic notions that later enabled Poincaré's great intuitions to be fully articulated in a mathematical way.

[13] G.P. Marsh, *Man and nature*, Scrivener, New York, 1864. The passage is from the section entitled Nothing Small in Nature (pp. 643-4) which concludes Chap. IV.

environment. Models of systems which are highly sensitive to initial conditions are useful for predicting scenarios that we would like to spare future generations. Marsh, in fact, observed that:

> (…)our inability to assign definite values to these causes of the disturbance of natural arrangements is not a reason for ignoring the existence of such causes in any general view of the relations between man and nature, and we are never justified in assuming a force to be insignificant because its measure is unknown, or even because no physical effect can now be traced to it as its origin.[13]

I emphasize *now*. The author of *Man and Nature* (1864) points out that time plays a role in the case of the 'perverse and unexpected' consequences of our activities (perturbations of human origin) in a system highly sensitive to initial conditions. He seems to be referring to clock time, but the time of human technology is not the same as the time of nature. When Marsh warned of the risks of clearing forests, he was well aware that:

> (…) the growth of arboreal vegetation is comparatively slow, and we are often told that, though he who buries an acorn may hope to see it shoot up to a miniature resemblance of the majestic tree which shall shade his remote descendants, yet the longest life hardly embraces the seedtime and the harvest of a forest.[15]

This creates an intellectual revolution, a change in gestalt, in our models of economic development. As I have written elsewhere,[16] an organism that,

---

[14] In chapter 4 of *Science and method*, Poincaré gives another interesting example from the kinetic theory of gases. He invites us to imagine a gas consisting of many molecules which move around inside a container at high speed. They strike the walls and collide with each other. These collisions occur under a wide variety of conditions. If a molecule were to deviate slightly to the left or right of its trajectory, it would avoid a collision or undergo a collision, which would cause its direction to change by, say, 90° or 180°. A molecule would continue to collide a great many times per second, so that if the first collision multiplied its deviation by a large number A, after n collisions, the deviation would be multiplied by A^n. The deviation would become enormous, not only because A is a large number, that is, because small events cause large effects, but also because the exponent n is large, that is, because the collisions are numerous and the events complex.

[15] G.P. Marsh, *Man and nature*, Scrivener, New York, 1864, Chap. III.

[16] E. Tiezzi, *Il capitombolo di Ulisse*, Feltrinelli, Milan, 1991, Chap. 7, where this concept of Clausius is discussed.

for its subsistence, consumes faster than its environment produces, cannot survive for long; it has chosen a dead branch of the tree of evolution. The opposite choice is to respect the biophysical constraints necessary for the conservation of nature. In 1885, Clausius wrote that there was a general law for national economies, namely, that more than is produced in a given period must not be consumed in the same period. This meant that only the quantity of fuel that could be replaced in the same period by tree growth should be consumed.[16] This type of caution is incompatible with the modern value 'time is money', based on clock time and inappropriate for establishing a correct relationship with nature. According to Marsh,

> The planter of a wood, it is said, must be actuated by higher motives than those of an investment, the profits of which consist in direct pecuniary gain to himself or even to his posterity; for if, in rare cases, an artificial forest may, in a generation or two, more than repay its original cost, still, in general, the value of its timber will not return the capital expended and the interest accrued.

Marsh concluded that operations of this kind had to be part of a policy which transcended short-term interests of individuals and fulfilled "duties of this century towards future centuries".[15]

'This century' meant the nineteenth century. At the end of the twentieth century these duties did not seem to have been done. As we have already seen, the gap between technological time and biological time has become an abyss.

The use of the mathematics of chaos, fractal geometry[17] and models based on far-from-equilibrium dynamics is one of the complex and difficult paths necessary in order to unravel the mysteries of the ecological network.

Far from equilibrium: small fluctuations and macroscopic divergence

As underlined above, in order to understand the real world we have to go beyond the thermodynamics of equilibrium states.

---

[17] Fractal geometry is the geometry of deterministic chaos and may describe the geometry of mountains, clouds and galaxies (B. Mandelbrot, Fractals, a geometry of nature, in N. Hall (ed.), *Chaos*, pp. 119-132). Fractals, moreover, are beautiful (see for example H.O. Peitgen & P.H. Richter, *La bellezza dei frattali*, Italian translation, Bollati Boringhieri, Turin, 1987). I shall not go into the question here; the reader is referred to my book, *Il capitombolo di Ulisse*, Chap. 2.

The British physical chemist Peter Coveney[18] wrote that all processes occur in a finite time and therefore outside equilibrium. In theory, a system can only tend towards equilibrium but will never reach it. It is therefore curious that scholars of thermodynamics concentrated their attention on equilibrium states. The difference between equilibrium and non-equilibrium is the same as that between a journey and its destination, or the words of a sentence and the full stop at the end. A system only reaches equilibrium by virtue of irreversible non-equilibrium processes. Life itself is a non-equilibrium process; ageing is irreversible and equilibrium is reached only at death, when the body returns to dust. An iron bar with its ends initially at different temperatures is an example of a system in non-equilibrium. The temperature gradient along the bar

---

[18] P. Coveney, Chaos, entropy and the arrow of time, in *Chaos – a science for the real world*, N. Hall (ed), Italian translation F. Muzzio, Padua, 1992. Here it is perhaps worthwhile summarizing the meaning of this chapter. Much work by physicists and mathematicians this century has concerned reversibility/irreversibility and the need to reconcile determinism and the reversibility of Newton's equations with the statistical and irreversible pattern of physical systems. Initially it was thought that the objective involved making a transition from the laws of dynamics of a system with many degrees of freedom to the laws of thermodynamics via a statistical definition of entropy. In the last twenty years, much progress has been made in this field. The problem has been framed in completely new terms and on a rigorous mathematical basis. A new type of motion, termed stochastic or intrinsic motion, has been discovered. This term indicates the motion of a dynamic system which, while governed by rigorously deterministic laws, behaves as if the system were under the effect of purely random forces. Stochastic motion is therefore highly chaotic, irregular and unpredictable. It provides a link between the statistical and dynamic laws of physics, once regarded as contradictory. It also makes it possible to derive the former from the latter. A feature of stochastic motion is the extreme instability of the solutions in response to changes in initial conditions or external perturbations. For example, the motion of a gas molecule under normal conditions of temperature and pressure is completely different after less than 50 collisions, if we consider the perturbation caused by the gravitational field of an electron on the other side of the universe, i.e. 10^{10} light years away. These brief considerations illustrate the relative importance of determinism and the reversibility of the laws of classical physics: the tiniest error in the initial data produces a completely different solution. More than a century ago, Maxwell had the insight that the same antecedents do not produce the same consequences. He added that this concept was of little use in a world such as ours, in which the same antecedents never occur and nothing happens twice. He exhorted physicists to study singularities and instabilities in order to overcome the prejudice in favour of determinism, which seemed to arise from the assumption that the physics of the future would merely be an enlargement of that of the past.

normally equalizes, establishing a situation of equilibrium. However if we keep one end at a higher temperature, a continuous thermodynamic force is exerted on the bar, a temperature gradient which produces a flow of heat along the bar. The entropy production of the bar is the product of the force (temperature gradient) and the heat flow.[18]

In the 1920s, Lars Onsager at Yale University began to study systems close to equilibrium in which the flow is a linear function of the force (if force doubles, so does flow). In 1945 Prigogine at Brussels University formulated the 'theorem of minimum entropy production' which states that near-equilibrium systems evolve towards a steady state in which dissipation is at a minimum. Later he and Paul Glansdorff tried to extend the theorem to systems far from equilibrium, in which the linearity between force and flow is lost. In far-from-equilibrium systems, the smallest fluctuations can lead to completely different macroscopic behaviour. One of the main results of the Brussels group was that steady states far from equilibrium can become unstable if taken even further from equilibrium, when a bifurcation is possible in which the system prefers to move away from the steady state and evolves towards some other stable state.[18]

If a cascade of bifurcations is created, more than one stable state is possible. These non-uniform states of structural organization that vary in time or space or both are the dissipative structures analysed by Prigogine and his school. Their self-organization has an interesting philosophical consequence. It suggests that we re-examine the association of the direction of time and uniform degeneration towards randomness, at least at a local level; at the 'end' of time, at equilibrium, randomness may have the last word, but in a shorter temporal scale it is possible to observe the development of wonderfully ordered structures which last for as long as the flow of matter and energy.

Shadows of Penrose

In *Shadows of the Mind*, the English theoretical physicist Roger Penrose, known for his study of black holes, went deeper into the questions he had dealt with in his book *The Emperor's New Mind*,[19] questions which brought the behaviour of the brain, as an integral part of the history of nature, into the mainstream of physics. He criticised the opinion that the

[19] R. Penrose, *The emperor's new mind*, Oxford University Press, Oxford, 1989.

mechanisms of artificial intelligence can lead to results similar to those of the human mind. He traced the basis of a new physics which incorporates the behaviour of the cosmos and the complexity of cognitive mechanisms and neurons.

The history of co-evolution of our planet cannot have developed different strategies for cognitive and evolutionary processes, since the former are part of the latter. Today, faced with the intriguing complexity of the history of biological evolution, research into complex systems can only proceed by accentuating the evolutionary and systemic character of the theoretical foundations of physics and the other sciences.

Penrose[20] ventures into the realm of the 'shadows of the mind', beyond Einstein's idea of space-time, in an attempt to relate quantum mechanics, general relativity and Einstein's gravitation. He considers that the present formulation of quantum mechanics cannot explain phenomena such as black holes, and argues in favour of a physics closer to the real world, sustained by the laws of irreversibility and more in tune with the physical behaviour of the biological world (cells, cell structure, neurons, biochemical mechanisms). He expresses the hope that mathematics, biology and physics will pool their results in a global view of nature.

Penrose claims that our lack of knowledge of the basic laws of physics prevents us from understanding the mind in physical and logical terms. Prigogine would probably add that this difficulty is related to the survival of Cartesian dualism in today's physics. The usual formulation of the laws of physics implies time symmetry and determinism, whereas life and the brain require an evolutionary approach and imply the appearance of novelty.

The proposals of Penrose and Prigogine, though different, have the courage to transgress by contaminating physics with ecology, logic with biology and cosmology with psychology. Even in the most advanced studies of epistemology and ecological modelling, one often observes a 'scientific' fear of transgression, a call to stay within the confines of a certain paradigm or science, to 'observe' the rules on which the validity of a certain discipline depends. Two major scholars of complexity, Marcello Cini in Italy and Howard Odum in the United States, known for criticising mechanistic paradigms and building new models, respectively, have often held back, I believe, not sharing the view that knowledge of

---

[20] R. Penrose, *Shadows of the mind – a search for the missing science of consciousness*, Oxford University Press, Oxford, 1994.

reality and nature cannot be a slave to paradigms or preconstituted rules, and must be nourished by many points of view: a mixing of languages, methodologies and approaches related by feedback and co-evolution.

In this way a little scientific rigour will be lost in favour of greater creativity in the processes of knowledge; science will at last be free and no longer homogenizing and schematic. It will then be possible to write different and eccentric histories of space and time,[21] to think up theories of evolution with no foundations,[22] to compare historical time with biological time, and to go beyond the counterposition of events and paradigms, nature and scientific laws, atoms and ecosystems.[23] Modern philosophical and scientific thought were moulded by the need to build a cosmos, to rediscover order.[22] Today, awareness of biodiversity, of the existence of relations on this planet at risk, and of the fact that co-evolution moulded history, suggest a narrative view of an indeterminate universe as basis for a necessarily *evolutionary physics*..

---

[21] G. Bocchi and M. Ceruti, *Origini di storie*, Feltrinelli, Milan, 1993.

[22] M. Ceruti, *Evoluzione senza fondamenti*, Laterza, Rome and Bari, 1995.

[23] E. Tiezzi (ed.), *Ecologia e ...*, Laterza, Bari, 1995.

12

LINGER, FAIR PASSING MOMENT![1]

Community with the future

Ecological science is concerned with the biosphere as a whole, with its relations and its problems of sustainability. To introduce the concept of sustainability, it is useful to start from the theories of the steady state economy of Herman Daly.[2] By way of example, Daly considers the problem of loading a boat. With the cargo distributed in an optimum way, the maximum load can be carried. However, there is still a limit to the weight the boat can carry, even with optimum stowing. In an economy, the price system may distribute prices evenly, but unless there is some external constraint, it will continue to do so until the optimally loaded boat sinks. This example illustrates the concept of the limited capacity of the Earth; the economy must accept the biophysical limits imposed by the closed thermodynamic system in which we live.

In defining the steady state, Daly starts with the First Principle of Thermodynamics, namely, that energy and matter cannot be created or destroyed, only transformed. Man transforms primary materials into goods and goods into wastes. Daly then considers the Second Principle of Thermodynamics and entropy to define the constraints and flows of an open system in a steady state or in biophysical equilibrium with the external environment. He identifies the main physical coordinate of scarcity in the Second Principle. Were it not for the law of entropy, there would be no losses; we could burn the same litre of petrol forever, and our economic system need not be related to the world of nature. If we take the term 'growth' to indicate a quantitative change and the term

---

[1] From an archaic English translation of J. W. von Goethe's *Faust*.

[2] H.E. Daly quoted in E. Tiezzi, *L'equilibrio. I diversi aspetti di un unico concetto*, Cuen, Naples, 1995.

'development' to indicate a qualitative change, then a steady state economy develops but does not grow, just like the Earth, of which the human economy is a subsystem. Sufficient wealth, maintained and allocated efficiently, distributed equably (rather than maximizing production) is a good economic aim.

Ethical values and biophysical constraints thus find a way of converging in the steady state economy or the economy in biophysical equilibrium. Ten years after its formulation, theoretical elaboration of this idea led to the concept of sustainable development. The new theories of sustainable development and ecological economics provide a new paradigm: an economy no longer based on two parameters, labour and capital, but an ecological economy which recognizes the existence of three parameters, labour, natural capital and man-made capital. If natural capital is defined as the set of natural systems (seas, rivers, lakes, forests, flora, fauna, land) together with the products of agriculture, fishing, hunting and gathering and the cultural and artistic heritage, it is evident that today we must invest in natural capital.

According to Daly, there are two obvious principles of sustainable development for the management of renewable resources. The first is that the rate of consumption should be equal to the rate of regeneration (sustainable yield). The second is that the rate of production of wastes should be equal to the natural capacity of the ecosystems in which they are discharged to absorb them. The regeneration and absorption capacities must be regarded as natural capital, and failure to maintain and observe these capacities must be regarded as consumption of capital and hence not sustainable.

Herman Daly[3] abandons the certainties of orthodox economics and the determinism of the 'invisible hand of the market' when he tackles the theme of ecological complexity in these terms. There are two ways of maintaining total capital constant. The sum of man-made and natural capital can be maintained constant in value, or each component can be maintained separately. The first way is reasonable if one regards man-made and natural capital as interchangeable. In this view it is entirely acceptable to divest natural capital as long as one creates an equivalent value in man-made capital by investment. The second way is reasonable if one considers that man-made and natural capital complement each

---

[3] H.E. Daly, ISEE Conference, Stockholm, August 1992: Operationalizing sustainable development by investing in natural capital.

other. The complements must each be maintained (separately or jointly in fixed proportion) because the productivity of one depends on the availability of the other. The first case is called 'weak sustainability' and the second, 'strong sustainability'. Man-made and natural capital are fundamentally complementary and only marginally interchangeable. Therefore strong sustainability is ultimately the relevant concept, although weak sustainability is a useful first step.

The flow of natural resources and the natural capital stock that generates it are the material basis of production; the capital stock that transforms raw material inputs into product outputs is the effective basis of production. One cannot substitute effective basis for material basis; one cannot build the same wooden house with half the timber no matter how many saws and hammers one tries to substitute.

Certain biases seem to have kept us from seeing the obvious, namely, that the catch of fish is limited by the numbers and size of fish populations still in the sea, not by the number of fishing boats; timber production is limited by the remaining forests, not by sawmills. More sawmills and more fishing boats do not result in more timber cut and more fish caught. For that you need more forests and larger fish populations in the sea. Natural capital and man-made capital are complementary; and natural capital has become the limiting factor. More man-made capital, far from being interchangeable with natural capital, just puts greater complementary demands on it, running it down faster to temporarily support the value of man-made capital, making it all the more limiting in the future.

Today we are living in a time of transition between an 'empty world' economy and a 'full world' economy. In the latter, the only pathway to sustainability involves investing in the scarcest resource, the limiting factor. Sustainable development means investing in natural capital and in scientific research into global biogeochemical cycles that underlie the sustainability of the biosphere.

What is implied by the view that natural capital and man-made capital are complementary and not interchangeable? It implies that whichever is less will become the limiting factor. If they were interchangeable, neither could be a limiting factor because productivity of one would not depend on availability of the other. The idea that either natural or man-made capital can be limiting factors does not arise if we continue to think that they can replace each other. Once we realise that they are complementary, we have to ask which of the two is the limiting factor, that is, which is less available.

This line of reasoning implies that the Earth is in a transition from an era in which man-made capital was the limiting factor to an era in which natural capital is the limiting factor. Daly goes on to point out that the quantity of crude oil extracted today is limited by the availability of oil in the wells (or by the capacity of the atmosphere to absorb carbon dioxide), not by the capacity to extract it. Agricultural production is often limited by the availability of water, not by that of tractors and harvesters. We are in a transition from a world relatively rich in natural capital and with relatively little man-made capital (and men) to a world poor in the former and rich in the latter.

In a production process, a flow of material and energy of natural origin is transformed into a flow of final products by a number of agents and transformations, namely, labour and capital. Capital and labour are interchangeable up to a certain point, because their qualitative function in a production process is the same: they are both agents of transformation of the flow of primary materials into finished products. However, the qualitative roles of resources and capital are quite different, the same difference that exists between the transformer and the transformed, between stock and flow.

Daly identifies three approaches:
1. economic imperialism, which is when the economic system incorporates the ecosystems, placing the flows of materials and energy under the influence of prices;
2. ecological reductionism, which is when the economic system is treated as a subsystem of the ecosystem;
3. the steady state, in which the flows of materials and energy between the economy and the environment are limited by sustainability.

In the past era of the 'empty world' economy, man-made capital was the limiting factor, as we have seen. In the approaching era of the 'full world' economy, natural capital will be the limiting factor. Sustainable development requires that natural renewable capital be maintained constant. There is also the category of non-renewable resources, which strictly speaking cannot be maintained constant except by not consuming them, or not regarding them as resources, even for the future. They can, however, be exploited in a quasi-sustainable way, controlling the rate of their exploitation on the basis of a correct comparison with the rate of creation of renewable substitutes. The quasi-sustainable use of non-renewable resources requires that every exploitation of a non-renewable resource be balanced by a compensatory investment in a renewable substitute (for example, the extraction of crude oil be balanced by the cultivation of trees for wood alcohol production).

Daly speaks of three types of community: community between people, community with other species and community with future generations. After criticising the growth-orientated economics that have led to the present environmental disasters, he lays the basis for a new economics, or rather, for a new social ethic. The foundation of this ethic is community with the future (or generational solidarity), necessary in order to leave our grandchildren a planet which can still sustain community life. This brings us to the concept of sustainability, sustainable lifestyle and sustainable development.

'Sustainability' means the set of relations between human activity and its dynamics, and the biosphere and its dynamics, which are generally slower. These relations must be such as to enable human life to continue, individuals to satisfy their needs and different human cultures to develop, but in such a way that the effects of human activity on nature stay within certain limits and do not destroy the global biophysical context.

Time, relation and constraints

The scientific novelty is that the system in which we live, the planet Earth, is a finite system, and as such it has constraints in terms of land, life cycles (air, water, oxygen and so forth) and absorption of wastes and pollutants, which limit the indiscriminate increase of population and production. The physical world is subject to constraints which determine limits. For example, if the population increases, more food is needed, which means producing more food per hectare or cultivating more land. The first solution means impoverishment of the soil, erosion, pollution of the aquifer and eutrophication of the seas; the second means clearing forests to provide more arable land, loss of biodiversity, alteration of the carbon and oxygen cycles (increased greenhouse effect), climatic changes which in turn affect agriculture, and so forth.

Economic programming must therefore operate within these constraints, in tune with natural rhythms and the dynamics of global biogeochemical cycles. It is a problem of relations and interdependence. Ecology is known as the science of relations and complexity, and it requires different specialisations which interact with each other. Constraints are defined as the carrying capacity of the planet, that is, the planet's capacity to carry or sustain the human population and all the other forms of life (plants and animals) needed by man and nature to survive. This is the basis of sustainability.

The Earth cannot therefore be viewed as belonging to us and as being for our exploitation, but as a natural capital entrusted to us by our parents for our children. The Earth was here long before us, and has 4,500 million years of evolution behind it. The history of biological evolution is a complex history of energy, matter, molecules and cells which gave rise to a great diversity of life forms. Many biological species multiplied on the Earth's surface, or in the biosphere, by virtue of the continuous flow of solar energy and photosynthesis. This is the natural capital entrusted to us, the capital of biodiversity made of air, earth, rivers, seas, forests and animals. Biodiversity is essential for the maintenance of life, because everything is linked to everything on this planet. The cultural challenge of the third millenium is that of maintaining this heritage for our children. It is simultaneously a scientific and an ethical challenge, a challenge we cannot afford to ignore.

Until now, economics has rightly used the First Law of Thermodynamics and the conserved quantities, energy and mass, to deal with man-made capital, such as cars. Orthodox economics has adopted all the theoretical equipment of the doctrine of mechanical determinism, including time reversibility. Natural capital which could be ignored yesterday, but which has now become a limiting factor, belongs to another logical type, that of systems far from equilibrium, complex evolving systems. Like entropy, dissipating structures, irreversible processes and dynamic chaos, natural capital must therefore be treated in evolutionary terms rather than in terms of energy-mass conservation. The constructive role of time and probability must be fully understood. In simple terms, this means replacing classical physics with evolutionary physics in economics and ecology.

A first attempt to do this was made by Matthias Ruth, who framed the relation between ecology and economics in terms of the laws of thermodynamics. Our group of ecodynamics at the University of Siena subsequently introduced several sustainability indicators based on relations between energy and entropy and a new function derived from Odum's emergy, known as free emergy, similar to the Gibbs function.

The sustainability indices are for open thermodynamic systems.

As underlined by Matthias Ruth,[4] economies are open systems contained in an ecosystem (the biosphere) with which we exchange matter and energy. Economic systems and ecosystems are both in a steady state, far from equilibrium, and only dynamic evolutionary models based on irreversible, non-conserved quantities and functions can enable us to understand the complexity of the interactions between natural and man-made capital, between biosphere and system of production, between nature (of which we are part) and economic activity. This is the challenge of physics, economics and ecology for the new millenium. It will take place in the field of thermodynamics and its protagonist will be time.

In taking up this challenge, it will be necessary to resist the dual temptations of reductionism: that of separating the parts and eliminating relations, and that of separating a thing from its evolution, seeing it in a static way in the isolated moment that does not exist in nature. Time irreversibility and time asymmetry are intrinsic properties of nature and govern relations. An elementary particle does not exist alone in a given instant but in relation to other particles and its environment, in the flux of time, in its Lucretian 'clinamen'. Freeman Dyson put it well when he spoke of the need to write the evolutionary history of molecules. Henry-Louis Bergson wrote that if time were not invention, it was nothing. Creativity is the prime mover of life and biological evolution.

An oxymoron

'Linger, fair passing moment!' is a paradoxical title. As St. Augustine taught, the past and future do not exist (one was, the other will be)[5] and the eternal present is nothing more than a fleeing moment. Nevertheless we should like to stop the moment because it encompasses both stability and change. This paradox was apprehended by George Perkins Marsh in a long note which concludes his masterpiece:

> No atom can be disturbed in place, or undergo any change of temperature, of electrical state, or other material condition, without affecting, by attraction or repulsion or other communication, the surrounding atoms. These, again, by the same law, transmit the influence to other atoms, and the

---

[4] M. Ruth, *Integrating economics, ecology and thermodynamics*, Kluwer, Dordrecht, 1993.
[5] St. Augustine, *Confessions*, Book XI, 14.17.

impulse thus given extends through the whole material universe. Every human movement, every organic act, every volition, passion, or emotion, every intellectual process, is accompanied with atomic disturbance, and hence every such movement, every such act or process, affects all the atoms of universal matter. Though action and reaction are equal, yet reaction does not restore disturbed atoms to their former place and condition, and consequently the effects of the least material change are never cancelled, but in some way perpetuated, so that no action can take place in physical, moral, or intellectual nature, without leaving all matter in a different state from what it would have been if such action had not occurred. Hence, to use language which I have employed on another occasion: there exists, not alone in the human conscience or in the omniscience of the Creator, but in external nature, an ineffaceable, imperishable record, possibly legible even to created intelligence, of every act done, every word uttered, nay, of every wish and purpose and thought conceived by mortal man, from the birth of our first parent to the final extinction of our race; so that the physical traces of our most secret sins shall last until time shall be merged in that eternity of which not science, but religion alone, assumes to take cognizance.[6]

The puritan Marsh was certain of that eternity, whereas our religion is more related to uncertainty (if only for the reasons set out in Chapter 5). As I wrote elsewhere, my secularism means that I regard matter, energy and their interactions as the basis of the origin and continuance of life: the sacred is in matter. This very statement, however, makes profound love of nature possible.[7] To love nature means not dispersing the memory of past actions and events, as Marsh writes, all of which are embodied in the present, or resorting to cheap utopias, but taking responsibility as inhabitants of time. Gottfried Benn put it well in 1949, when he wrote that only the moment has value, only the mood counts, only the impression is right, only the tragic lasts.[8]

---

   [6] G.P. Marsh, *Man and nature*, Scrivener, New York, 1864, Footnote to the section, "Nothing small in nature" of Chap. VI, pp. 643-4.

   [7] E. Tiezzi, *Il capitombolo di Ulisse*, Feltrinelli, Milan, 1991, Chapter 3.

   [8] G. Benn, *Pietra, verso, flauto*, J.P. Wallmann (ed.), Italian translation by G. Forti, Adelphi, Milan, 1990, from a letter of 24th August 1949 to Nele Poul Sorensen.

Our tragedy, or rather that of our civilization, has already been discussed (Ch. 7, Like the face of the moon). According to Goethe, our salvation lies in our capacity to perceive beauty. When we say, as Faust did, "Linger, fair passing moment!" it is as if we issue an invitation to disobey. Our plea is an oxymoron: 'linger' presupposes conservation, 'moment' implies irreversibility and presupposes evolution; otherwise, how can the passing moment be fair?

APPENDIX

ECODYNAMICS

Prigogine's arrow of time and Large Poincaré Systems

As we saw in Chapters 6 and 11, Prigogine[1] regards the biosphere as a large system far from equilibrium, in which instability, bifurcations, dissipative structures and chaotic structures play an essential role. Non-equilibrium thermodynamics is used to describe atmospheric processes and, according to Prigogine, is a fundamental aid in the study of the biosphere.

Prigogine holds that time is real and plays a basic constructive role in nature; the arrow of time is associated with dynamic instability. For unstable systems, proximity to equilibrium is associated with an increase in entropy; hence for this type of process it is possible to attribute a microscopic meaning to irreversibility. However, in more general cases, such as processes far from equilibrium, the situation is different.

Prigogine used Poincaré's theorem of 1889 to make an alternative formulation of dynamics described in terms of probabilities. This description introduces the arrow of time into physics. Prigogine reflects that the cosmological arrow of time and the biological arrow of time are everyday terms. With this new description, he and his team hoped to have identified the common root of all these arrows of time. At the beginning of their theory, they hoped to be able to apply it in a concrete way to the problems of ecology.

Systemic and evolutionary approaches, or to use a term we have coined at the University of Siena, ecodynamic models, are required for the major

---

[1] I. Prigogine, in: C. Rossi and E. Tiezzi (eds), *Ecological physical chemistry*, Elsevier, Amsterdam, 1991, pp. 1-24.

problems of ecology (increased greenhouse effect, the hole in the ozone layer, acid rain, eutrophication). These models are necessarily based on the thermodynamics of Prigogine, on the science of dissipative chaos and far-from-equilibrium processes.

Returning to the theorem of Poincaré, Prigogine reflects that Poincaré asked himself whether the physical universe was isomorphic to a system of non-interacting units. Energy (the Hamiltonian, H) is generally written as the sum of two terms: the kinetic energy of the units involved and the potential energy of their interactions. Poincaré asked whether the interactions could be eliminated. This is a very important question. If the answer is 'yes', then there may be no coherence in the universe. It was therefore lucky that he proved that interactions cannot generally be eliminated, because of resonances between the various units.

The Brussels school worked for years on these problems, identifying a class of dynamic systems known as Large Poincaré Systems (LPS),[1] for which it is possible to eliminate Poincaré divergence and 'integrate' a class of non-integrable Poincaré systems. An LPS is a system with a continuous spectrum, characterized by interactions involving integrations over resonances. These LPS are not integrable in the usual sense because of Poincaré resonance, but can be integrated by new methods by eliminating any Poincaré divergence.

Since we are dealing with chaotic systems, chance plays an increasing role and time symmetry is broken. This means that irreversibility is in the very core of this new dynamics. Prigogine observes that the usual time paradox is somehow inverted. Normally one tried to deduce the arrow of time from dynamics based on time-reversible equations. Now we generalize the dynamics to include irreversibility. The Poincaré divergences are eliminated by appropriate time ordering of the dynamical states. Two classes of LPS can be distinguished. In the first class, the canonical equations of motion in classical mechanics or the Hilbert space in quantum mechanics are time ordered. The results are trajectories of wave functions which are no longer symmetrical with respect to time. This is the simplest example unifying dynamics and thermodynamics. In the second class, the Poincaré divergence can be eliminated by time ordering of the statistical description, to obtain equations for the evolution of the probability distribution. The trajectories behave in a chaotic manner, whereas the probability distribution satisfies a simple diffusion-type equation. The Poincaré divergence leads to trajectories or wave functions which are both irreversible and stochastic.

In classical mechanics, we deal with numbers, whereas in quantum mechanics we deal with operators. In quantum mechanics, the Hamiltonian H is associated with eigenvalues of eigenfunctions. The set of eigenvalues of the eigenfunctions is called a spectral representation. This is a key problem of quantum mechanics and can be solved in only a few simple situations; usually perturbation methods have to be used. For non-integrable Poincaré systems, expansion of the eigenfunctions and eigenvalues into powers of the coupling constant leads to what is called the Poincaré catastrophe, due to the divergence associated with small denominators. Conventional perturbation methods do not solve the problem. In order to make non-integrable Poincaré systems 'integrable', Prigogine introduces 'natural time ordering' of dynamical states. As we saw in Chapter 8, this means that first we have the unstable atomic state, and then emission of radiation. This corresponds to Bohr's picture in which the radiation emitted by the atom is a 'delayed' wave.

To introduce time ordering, the Brussels school uses Boltzmann's statistical description. Obviously Boltzmann did not know the theory of chaos more than a century ago, and could not have imagined that he was studying non-integrable Poincaré systems. Like Maxwell, he invested his hopes in ergodic theory, which is very useful for understanding equilibrium, but is no good for dynamical purposes. Prigogine refers to sets introduced by J.W. Gibbs in the early period of statistical mechanics. Gibbs ensembles are obtained from a consideration of relations between particles; the particles collide and the collisions give rise to binary and then to higher-order relations in time.

Prigogine illustrates this question with the example of the glass of water. The glass contains the arrow of time in the sense that new relationships are created involving more and more particles of water. 'Old' water can be distinguished from 'new' water. This flow of correlations oriented in time breaks the symmetry of time involved in the classical description.

Let us imagine a transition from state A at time zero, characterized by no correlations, to state B at time t, characterized by many correlations. The transition from A to B involves different physical processes from the inverse transition from B to A.

Time ordering of correlations must be introduced into dynamics to avoid the Poincaré catastrophe and so that dynamics can be described in terms of the temporal evolution of the correlations. This involves a genuine change in gestalt with respect to classical dynamics; we are no longer studying the positions and momentum of particles in on-going time but following the evolution of the relations between particles, as conceived by Prigogine in 1962 in his essay *Non equilibrium statistical mechanics.*[2]

The ensemble theory of Gibbs has an equation for the time evolution of density matrix, which is formally similar to Schrödinger's equation:

$$i \frac{\partial \rho}{\partial t} = L\rho$$

where L is the Liouville operator, which can be expressed in terms of the Hamiltonian H both in classical and statistical mechanics.

A collision is a complex process in which particles approach each other, exchange energy by resonance and continue in different directions. A collision can be imagined as a sequence of states related by resonance. Prigogine writes that in a Hamiltonian system, a collision is not an instantaneous point event, but is extended in space and time; the spectrum of the Liouville operator is determined essentially by collision dynamics. This deviates radically from the usual methods of dynamics which hold for integrable systems, in which evolution can be resolved into a series of instantaneous events in space and time. This is why the dynamics of LPS can be formulated only at a statistical level; it cannot be reduced to trajectories as in classical dynamics or to wave functions as in quantum mechanics.

The integration of non-integrable Poincaré systems thus becomes the basis of a new evolutionary physics which includes irreversibility and broken time symmetry. The time paradox is eliminated; in the old situation, there was no bridge between the reversible microscopic level and the irreversible macroscopic one. Now we have a new unstable microscopic level with broken time symmetry, from which a dissipative macroscopic level emerges.

Dynamic chaos, non-equilibrium thermodynamics and more LPS

What we have said above leads to a better appreciation of the role of dynamic chaos. Phenomena such as friction and diffusion are based on

---

[2] I. Prigogine, *Non equilibrium statistical mechanics*, Wiley Interscience, New York, 1962.

the exchange of energy via collisions. They involve dissipative chaos (chemical chaos, turbulence). Prigogine emphasizes that dissipative chaos is part of the self-organization that appears in non-equilibrium and non-linear systems. Oscillating chemical reactions are an example.

The theory of non-linear dynamics has recently developed new methods of analysing complex systems. Recent experiments have revealed chaotic patterns arising from the non-linear nature of deterministic systems. By chaotic pattern we mean sensitivity to initial conditions. Chemical systems manifesting these phenomena range from organic reactions to metal alloys. There are chemical systems which show phenomena of self-organization such as the formation of stationary spatial structures or periodic oscillatory states.

Non-equilibrium thermodynamics shows that these phenomena are different modes of self-organization. The conditions necessary for these dissipative structures to appear are generally:
a) a critical distance from equilibrium;
b) a flow of matter and/or energy through the system;
c) appropriate non-linear kinetic laws.

These three conditions for the self-organization of non-equilibrium systems are often met in chemical and biological systems. Non-linear chemical systems often show a vast assortment of exotic dynamic phenomena if kept far from equilibrium. The Belousov-Zabotinsky reaction,[3] the best known system of this kind, shows a pattern that ranges from periodicity to quasi-periodicity, from intermittence to lack of phase, to chaos. Other chemical systems show similar dynamic phenomena. Whole families of oscillators based on the chemistry of halogens, calcogens and transition metals have been discovered. Oscillatory patterns have been observed in biochemical systems, such as enzyme reactions. Our group at Siena University has studied the closed unstirred Belousov-Zhabotinsky system.[4]

It can be concluded that the macroscopic order manifesting under non-equilibrium conditions is generated by dynamic chaos. As Prigogine puts it, there is order out of chaos, and, more generally, the fact that the basic description is in terms of non-integrable Poincaré systems shows us the variety of ways in which nature is present in our experience. Without

---

[3] See G. Nicolis and I. Prigogine, *Complexity*, Italian translation, Einaudi, Turin, 1991.

[4] N. Marchettini and M. Rustici, Effect of medium viscosity in a closed unstirred Belousov-Zhabotinsky system, *Chemical physics letters*, **317**, 647-51, 2000.

LPS, there would be no biosphere or science of ecology. An amusing analogy to be taken with a grain of salt is between the brain and nature. Recent research has shown that chaos plays a role in producing and transmitting information; for example, the formation of analogues of biomolecules rich in information by coupling their production with chaotic chemical reactions. It is also known that the electrical activity of the brain is substantially chaotic, so that mental illness may be due to too much regularity. In some ways nature acts like a giant brain that produces coherent structures in the macroscopic world through its chaotic microscopic state.[1]

This courageous analogy of Prigogine is in line with Jim Lovelock's studies on Gaia, the work of Lynn Margulis and the coevolutionary and systemic view of the new theories of the ecology of complexity.[5] In fact, LPS are evolving systems. Given the initial conditions, these systems go through different stages and diffusion processes. In this way, the evolution of systems is introduced into basic dynamics, which is obviously a fundamental step for the study of complex evolving ecosystems. Let us again consider the idea of Prigogine outlined in Chapter 8, namely that irreversibility is not related to Newtonian time or to its Einsteinian generalization, but to internal time, expressed in terms of relations between the various units that form the system, like relations between particles. We cannot stop the flow of relations, just as we cannot predict the decay of unstable atomic states. In the words of Nabokov: that which is real cannot be controlled, that which can be controlled is not real.[1]

At last the new evolutionary physics leaves the safe berth of determinism and subjectivity to incorporate uncertainty and irreversibility among its basic paradigms. In other words, it finally accepts the stochastic nature of time as an intrinsic property of matter. The views of classical and quantum mechanics based on the theories of integrable systems are simplified views. Anyone can see that nature has instabilities and chaos; physics can no longer ignore it.

I think Prigogine is right in considering that Poincaré's theorem of non-integrability will be considered as a turning point somewhat similar to the discovery that quantum mechanics was to the divergences of black

[5] J.E. Lovelock, *The age of Gaia. A biography of our living earth*, W.W. Norton & Company, Inc., New York, 1988; L. Margulis, *Symbiosis in cell evolution*, Freeman, New York, 1981; L. Margulis and R. Fester (eds), *Symbiosis as a Source of evolutionary innovation*, MIT Press, Cambridge, Mass., 1991.

body radiation in classical mechanics.[6] Poincaré divergences are leading us to a new formulation of dynamics.

[6] See, for example, T.S. Kuhn, *At the origins of contemporary physics. The theory of the black body and quantum discontinuity*, Italian translation, Il Mulino, Bologna, 1981.

EPILOGUE

GRANDFATHER, THE PHARMACIST
by Lidia Pulselli Tiezzi

My maternal grandfather was a pharmacist. He was a pharmacist in that he had a degree in Pharmacy and owned a pharmacy at Arcidosso, on Mt. Amiata, but he was an unlikely figure for his profession. Usually pharmacists are graduate-salesmen who like to sell their products, trying to convince customers that such and such a remedy is miraculous for such and such a disease. The truth is that my grandfather had little faith in the concoctions in his shop. He thought that a good chamomile tea (even if not picked on the night of St. John) and a good poultice of linseed were the thing for insomnia and bronchitis. He knew and loved an infinity of medicinal plants and had a good stock at home, should any member of his large family fall ill.

When I was little I spent the summer months at Arcidosso with my grandfather and aunts. I was good friends with our laundry woman, who went by the name of Evangelista. The town was famous for unlikely names; there was a girl called Folla Plaudente (applauding crowd), a boy called Anelito (gasping) and a little old man known by all as Beppe Fottilo (Giuseppe Fuck-him). The latter was actually registered as Giuseppe, but the other name had a story behind it. When he was about to be born, his father, already father of six children, was waiting outside with his head between his hands. A merry woman put her head out and announced: "Cheer up, Tono, you are the father of a bonny boy! What shall we call him?" "Call him Beppe and fuck him!!" was the reply of the father, overburdened by too many offspring.

Our laundry woman told the aunts about a very poor relative of hers who went to the pharmacy for a tonic for her sick husband. My grandfather read the prescription. "Listen, Marietta," he said, "with the money you would spend on this medicine, go and buy a good piece of meat for your husband and then go to Marianna in my name and get her to give you a flask of wine." Marianna was our factotum. Although charged with a thousand jobs, she even found the time to run a wine shop that my grandfather had provided for her.

There was such poverty at the time on the mountain, and it brought much apathy with it. I remember often going with my aunt to see a woman who was sick. I always tripped on the loose stones of the doorstep. The woman's husband was an unemployed mason who could not find the energy, in his long hours of idleness, to mortar the stones back into place. My grandfather said that medicine was the last thing they needed: "Good food and help when they are sick, and dentists!" Many women had bad teeth or no teeth at all. A popular verse ran: "Oh mountain girl, what happened to your teeth?" "Icy water and boiled chestnuts," was the reply. Chestnuts were the staple food. Aristotle (not the philosopher but Marianna's husband) used to tell about two friends who stopped at an inn for a glass of wine. One said: "If you were rich, what would you eat?" "A big plate of beans and pork rind! What about you?" "I don't know... the same, I guess!" Aristotle used to say that there was little money, but even fewer ideas.

When he was older, my grandfather retired and bought Laticastelli, a farm near Sienna. Here he began to live his real life. The manor house with its various farm buildings and the houses of the peasants were situated on a small rise. An avenue of cypresses wound majestically down to the main road. The view gave onto fertile fields that sloped away to the Ombrone River. On the other side, the lively relief of small hills of grey clay merged higher up with thick forests, populated by half-wild pigs. The clay hills produced wheat, and the forest provided much that was used by the peasants. Several families of peasants lived in charming houses with curious names: Spiritello, Spiritellino and Spiritellone.

I do not think my grandfather had a clue about farming but he was always about the fields, talking to the peasants and listening to them. He could not help reciting the odd verse of Virgil's *Georgics* or *Bucolics*, probably in Latin, but the peasants understood him, especially a certain Maggini. Maggini did not know Virgil but raised bees and spoke about them with an eloquence of his own, full of admiration and satisfaction, as if they were his dearest friends.

Grandfather rose early in the morning and drank a glass of milk. Often he got Beppa, his faithful maid, to make him a bruschetta with the new oil (toasted bread with recently-pressed olive oil). This oil was the main condiment he used.

When he bought Laticastelli he had some writing paper printed with the following letterhead:

Laticastelli Farm

Prop. Dr. Giovanni Battista Becchini

Producer of olive oil

"Better than butter for goodness and economy"

When he had finished his breakfast he would go about the fields and pathways collecting plants and stones. Very little escaped his gaze. Wandering for hours by himself, he never felt alone but was one with nature. He conversed with all creatures, animate and inanimate; he understood them and felt understood.

Sometimes he scrambled over the clay hills. In places the ground was bare of vegetation, and fossil shells were exposed here and there. With a special knife like a surgeon's scalpel he would gently free large scallop shells, shaped like the square of Siena, and harmoniously whorled murices from their grey clay prison. These beautiful ancient creatures spoke to him of remote eras. My grandfather had strong philosophical inclinations; he knew the world and its ugliness; he compared ancient and modern civilizations, noting that there had been no true progress. This disturbed him but he knew how to be patient in adversity and how to smile; he would see humour in the simplest things.

There was a large cellar with rows of enormous vats at Laticastelli. Each peasant put his grapes in a particular vat marked with a big sign: Oreste's vat, Benedetto's vat, Lorenzo's vat. Grandfather put signs on his vats too: Eleonora Duse's vat, Lyda Borelli's vat.

Many months of the year were spent in idyllic peace, but Grandfather did not forget his properties at Arcidosso. When the summer heat came, the aunts left for the mountain and he would join them shortly afterwards. In the town he was warmly welcomed; many families were related to him in some way and old friends and acquaintances were many. The house was an enormous old building which could accommodate many families; we spent happy days there among affectionate aunts and amusing uncles. Grandfather's properties included a series of fields and irrigated vegetable plots. Around Arcidosso there were many brooks and springs. When I woke in the mornings, the silence was unbroken and I could hear the silver sounds of water here and there. I would run to the window and open it to hear them more clearly, sounds that evoked cool glades. Nearest of all I could hear the gurgling of the Fonte della Vecchia, a fountain of wrought iron with many outlets, in the little square near the house.

Grandfather also owned a farm on Monte Labbro, which was another world: not a trickle of water, not a tree. Under the hot sun the earth produced short fragrant grass for the cattle. At the summit of Monte Labbro were the ruins of the house of Saint Davide.[1] On Mt. Amiata, Davide Lazzaretti was "Saint Davide". For a long time after his death he was remembered and secretly loved. He must have been a person of great magnetism. His rather confused doctrines of a sort of utopian mystic communism could hardly have had much power of persuasion, but people loved him and were fascinated by him.

In the house of one of our peasants there was a mysterious chest that was never opened. One day my girlish curiosity overcame the reluctance of the wife and she showed me clothes that the elders of the family had worn on that fateful day, 18th August 1878, when the followers of Saint Davide left Monte Labbro in procession for an unknown destination. When they reached Arcidosso they were ordered to halt; a rain of stones met them from one quarter and shots from another; Saint Davide was mortally wounded. Visibly moved, the old peasant woman showed me the red and blue cloaks, the pink and white veils, the coronets of flowers.

Filled with curiosity and awe, we would wander among the ruins of the rudimentary houses of the followers of Saint Davide. Here and there we came across the symbol of Davide, a Christian cross with an outward-facing crescent moon at each end of the horizontal, signifying that one way or another, everybody had his cross. Grandfather was reluctant to

---

[1] Davide Lazzaretti was born in Arcidosso (Grosseto) in 1834. Initially a carter, in 1868 visions led him to take up the hermit's life in a cave near Montorio Romano. Three months later he began to preach to the people of Mt. Amiata, claiming to have been called by God to restore original Christianity. In 1872 he founded the "Universal Jurisdavidic Church". After being tried and acquitted in 1871 and 1873, his movement, initially condoned by the ecclesiastic authorites, became progressively more millenarian and contentious. In 1878 the "prophet of Mt. Amiata" and his followers proclaimed their Republic of God on Mt. Labbro. On 18th August, Lazzaretti was killed during a procession to Arcidosso, forbidden by the authorities for public order. Curiously, the prophet used to wear a plate of armour on his chest, and he invited the carabinieri to aim at his heart. One of the projectiles hit him in the head.

answer my questions on Lazzaretti and would merely shake his head. I think he felt compassion for the tragic fate of the Prophet of Amiata and sympathy for his utopian ideas.

I knew an old follower of Saint Davide, by the name of Tommencioni. Often when my aunts and I were climbing among the shady chestnuts, we would cross his path. He would be coming down the steep track with his mountaineer's gait. He was old, lined and angular but tall and erect; his lively dark eyes were full of sparkle. "Do you recognize us?" Aunt Iole would ask. "Yes," he would reply, "you are the Tiste sisters." Since we were of the family of Signor Giovanni Battista, they called us the Tiste sisters. Tommencioni was a man of few words, but when he spoke it was in verse. For each of us he would improvise a rhyme as a sort of compliment and greeting. What tranquil days passed in peace with nature! An hour passed with a book or a toy in the shade of the chestnuts was a daily pleasure; to climb up to the rock of the Vettoraia was more of a task; to reach the Contessa's Field in search of raspberries was a walk lasting several hours. We all went on foot, of course; there were no roads and no cars. Anyone who wanted to reach the cross at the summit of Amiata had to go by mule. Late at night at the "Tonda" (rotunda) the participants would gather with the mules and muleteers whose job it was to lead the way and to get the mules, famous for their sense of independence, to collaborate. The mules would not wear saddles; on their back a light but unwieldy pack-saddle would be arranged. In order to stay there one leg had to go east and the other west. At the end of the journey, one's legs were terribly stiff. The summit was attained at dawn as the view unfolded. Three provinces lay below, stretching away to the sea. Now it can be reached easily by car, but Amiata is not the same; it is now a network of roads, roaring motors, bars and restaurants, and there are empty cans everywhere. My grandfather would have been upset to see nature contaminated in this way. Luckily he was able to enjoy a clean and simple countryside for many years. He died quietly one night at the age of 83 years, like a lamp with no more oil.

CLOSING WORD

We have seen that time 'tends not to be' (St. Augustine) and a theme which runs right thought this book is that our sense of time is derived from things themselves (Lucretius, *De rerum natura*, Book I). The epilogue was written by my mother, whose memories are full of nostalgia for 'things' that have been lost.

We remember and grieve for things that are no longer, things we ought to have saved from Time, the Destroyer. It is a losing battle and probably just as well, because it enables us to rethink our attitudes and ways of living. However, there is always the risk of becoming Chronos, the Destroyer, ourselves, such as when we forget the teachings of Sais. If we aspire to being more than the gravediggers of the Planet, a taste for connecting distant things must involve both science and poetry, understanding but also listening to nature. For centuries the Western tradition regarded the world as an enormous book written by divine wisdom. I would be happy enough today if we could find the rhymes in the poetry of nature. Garcia Lorca[1] expresses it much better than I.

Le onde
rimano con il sospiro
e la stella
con il grillo.

Trema sulla cornea
tutto il cielo freddo,
e il punto è una sintesi
dell'infinito.

Ma chi accorda onde
e sospiri,
stelle
e grilli?

Aspettate che i Geni
si distraggano un attimo.
Le chiavi scorrono
fra noi.

---

[1] Federico Garcia Lorca, Armonia, in *Sonetti dell'amore oscuro*, Italian translation by M. Socrate, Garzanti, Milan, 1985, p. 141.

Names index

The End of Time

E. TIEZZI, University of Siena, Italy

A best seller in Italy for two decades this influential title, which crucially and originally identified the core of ecological crisis in the difference between rapid technological tempos and slow biological tempos, has now been translated into English for the first time. Twenty years ago many were realizing that the issues surrounding energy and the environment would present the defining challenges for a generation. The first edition of this book emphasised the need to reconcile the wants and pace of a modern generation with the hard reality that evolutionary history had already pre-determined a pace of her own. Tiezzi explained the relevance of cleaner energy and the critical need to search for sociological solutions. Presenting scenarios of 'hard' and 'soft' sustainability for the future, he posed the critical question: Will the scientific and cultural instruments we have be enough to combat the pressures of unsustainable human behaviour?
Now fully revised and still highly relevant, this book will be of interest to technical and graduate audiences as well as general readers who wish to explore these issues further.
Series: The Sustainable World, Vol 1
ISBN: 1-85312-931-3   2002   apx 250pp
apx £79.00/US$122.00/€128.00

Find us at
http://www.witpress.com

US Mirror Site
http://www.compmech.com

Sustainable Energy

Y. PYKH and I.G. MALKINA-PYKH, Russian Academy of Sciences, Russia

Partial Contents: Energy Technology; Energy Planning and Policy; Energy and Society; Energy and the Global Environment; Future Global Aspects; Glossary of Terms.
Series: The Sustainable World, Vol 3
ISBN: 1-85312-939-9   2002   apx 150pp
apx £57.00/US$88.00/€92.00

Sustainable Water Resources

Y. PYKH and I.G. MALKINA-PYKH, Russian Academy of Sciences, Russia

This book, and its two companion volumes (see below), provide general guides for those in planning, administration, or other disciplines who require an overall view of the subjects involved.
Contents: History and Introduction; Systems Analysis of Water Systems; Natural Water Resources; Water Technology; Water Economics; Water and Society; Water and the Global Environment; Water and the Future; The Method of Response Function as a Modelling Tool; Glossary of Water Terms.
Series: The Sustainable World, Vol 5
ISBN: 1-85312-938-0   2002   apx 130pp
apx £49.00/US$75.00/€78.00

Multifunctional Landscapes

Volume I - Multifunctional Theory, Values and History

Editors: J. BRANDT, University of Roskilde, Denmark, and H. VEJRE, The Agricultural University, Copenhagen, Denmark

During the post-war period, intensified land use has been furthered primarily by spatial segregation of functions. Growing land pressure and environmental problems have made this strategy problematic and a paradigm of integrated multifunctional use of landscapes is emerging. This challenges a variety of disciplines and requires interdisciplinary cooperation on complex landscape research.

This book and its two companion volumes (see next column) present a collection of papers discussing these challenges from a variety of perspectives. All of the contributions also form the basis for a set of recommendations for future research within the three themes examined.

Volume 1 - Multifunctional Theory, Values and History focusses on future demands on the landscape concept, values and assessment of multifunctional landscapes, and ecological aspects of multifunctional landscapes in historical perspective.

Series: Advances in Ecological Sciences, Vol 14
ISBN: 1-85312-930-5   2002   apx 250pp
apx £85.00/US$131.00€137.00

All prices correct at time of going to press but subject to change.WIT Press books are available through your bookseller or direct from the publisher.

Multifunctional Landscapes

Volume II - Diversity and Management

Editors: J. BRANDT, University of Roskilde, Denmark, and H. VEJRE, The Agricultural University, Copenhagen, Denmark

This volume highlights monitoring multifunctional terrestrial landscapes, biodiversity versus landscape diversity in multifunctional landscapes, and complexity of landscape management.

Series: Advances in Ecological Sciences, Vol 15
ISBN: 1-85312-934-8   2002   apx 225pp
apx £75.00/US$116.00€121.00

Multifunctional Landscapes

Volume III - Continuity and Change

Editors: Ü. MANDER, University of Tartu, Estonia, and M. ANTROP, University of Gent, Belgium

A collection of papers discussing multifunctional landscape challenges from the perspective of continuity and change. Future recommendations for landscape planning and socio-economic programmes are included.

Series: Advances in Ecological Sciences, Vol 16
ISBN: 1-85312-935-6   2002   apx 400pp
apx £132.00/US$204.00€214.00
SET ISBN: 1-85312-936-4   apx £259.00/ US$399.00/€418.00 *(Over 10% saving)*